THE OU PROJECT GUIDE

Fieldwork and Statistics for Ecological Projects

by

Neil Chalmers and **Phil Parker**
Statistics Section
revised by
Kevin McConway

(*The Open University*)

together with the Open University *Ecology* Course Team (S326)
and staff of the Field Studies Council

Edited by
John Crothers
(*Field Studies Council*)

A Set Book for S326 *Ecology*

Published by
FIELD STUDIES COUNCIL

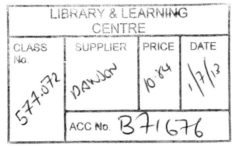

The authors wish to thank:—

Field Studies Council: Anne Bebbington and Paul Croft
Open University: Janet Evans, Peter Goodman, Dick Morris, Pat Murphy, Irene Ridge, Jonathan Silvertown, Peggy Varley and other members of the S326 course team

The editor wishes to thank (in addition to the above) John Archer-Thompson, John Bebbington, Robin Crump, Jim Fowler, John Hall, Sally Hayns, Jonathan Oldham, Robin Sutton, Tony Thomas and Steve Tilling.

Published by the Field Studies Council
No. 9 in a series of Occasional Publications

Second Edition (1989)

ISBN 1 85153 809 9

Printed by Henry Ling Ltd, The Dorset Press, Dorchester, Dorset

The scope of this guide

This Guide is intended for those faced with the challenge of devising and carrying out their own individual ecological project. It is assumed that you have some support from a tutor or supervisor, probably limited to infrequent contacts by phone or letter, and you may be unable to discuss step-by-step decisions and problems as they arise. Access to specialist equipment is probably also very limited. Above all, you will need to make effective use of your limited time.

The Guide is arranged in four chapters. The first explains the practical and theoretical issues you need to consider before you begin your project. Chapter 2 presents some information about statistical techniques that is of fundamental importance to the great majority of ecological projects. Chapters 3 and 4 describe specific practical and statistical techniques. No individual project is likely to require the use of more than a few of these techniques, and you are advised to read these Sections selectively. The decision chart printed on the inside back cover should guide you in your choice of statistical techniques.

We strongly advise that you read Chapters 1 and 2 before you start your project, so that you become familiar with the decision chart.

Contents

Chapter 1 Planning Ecological Projects

1.1 Practical considerations

Many excellent projects have been carried out by students with only limited time and resources at their disposal. However, ideas for worthwhile projects seldom come in inspirational flashes, and it is quite usual to feel totally bereft of ideas at the outset. Good projects often develop from making an initial perceptive observation in the field and then spending some time mulling over the possible significance of the observation and asking a wide variety of questions about the phenomenon.

For example, you might observe that your lawn has suffered from an invasion of moss. On closer examination, it seems that the moss proliferates more at one end of the lawn than at the other. Questions resulting from this observation could include:—

● Is the drainage better at one end than at the other?
● Is there more shade?
● Is the moss associated with the coarse grass growing at one end?
● Does more moss appear in turfed or in sown areas?
● Are there differences in soil properties at the two ends?
● Have the two parts of the lawn received different moss-control treatment in the past?
● Do the two parts experience different amounts of trampling?
● Does one end collect more cuttings when the lawn is mowed?

Each of these questions suggests a possible line of investigation. Some ideas can be discounted as trivial and not worth pursuing further; others seem to overlap and may be difficult to isolate in a single line of investigation (this is a common problem). Having considered as wide a range as possible, you can then narrow the suggestions down and devise a strategy for investigating the phenomenon. In this instance, your knowledge or background reading may encourage you to follow up the suggestion that drainage could be a major cause of the observed distribution of the moss. You have thus arrived at the point where you can formulate a **hypothesis**—a tentative explanation for the phenomenon which can be tested in some way—but at the same time remaining aware of the wide range of other possibilities during the course of your investigations. You can now embark on the first of the six steps of a research project as described in Section 1.3.

The range of observations you can make is, obviously, extremely wide; the following list gives some of the types of observation that may act as the starting point for an investigation—it is by no means an exhaustive list!

(i) Observations about species abundance—e.g. comparing different species within the same habitat, or of the same species between different habitats;
(ii) Observations about spatial patterns—e.g. demonstrating the non-randomness of distribution patterns (such as in a zonation) or of associations between species;
(iii) Observations about the distribution and abundance of species in relation to environmental factors;
(iv) Observations about species diversity in one or more habitats;
(v) Observations about temporal patterns, such as the diurnal rhythms of individual species or the seasonal changes in plant growth or animal activity.

There is a very great variety of possible ecological projects, but some are more "useful" than others. In deciding about your project, you should consider:

(a) *The total time available.* You must allow time for the essential work of planning and analysis, in addition to that spent on the actual fieldwork.

(b) *The periods available.* For some projects, you could concentrate the fieldwork into one or two days, collecting data and specimens to be analysed later at your convenience. For other projects you might need to spend short periods, probably at regular intervals, spread over many days or weeks. You must also decide whether your project needs to be carried out at a particular time of year, for which you would need to plan accordingly.

(c) *The localities available.* You should balance your interest in any particular project against the practical difficulties of getting to the site and carrying out the work; you may need to make more visits to the site than you originally planned. If you live near a stream, woodland or coast, these habitats present you with options which are much less accessible to the inland city dweller; however, many projects are possible in a city environment. Data may also be gathered from experiments carried out at home, which have been stimulated by the fieldwork.

(d) *Your own special interests.* If you are already knowledgeable about a particular topic, a relevant project will allow you to pursue that interest. Knowledge of certain groups of organisms can be very helpful, particularly when identifying species, since this step is often time-consuming for the novice.

Some of the common pitfalls in devising projects, which should be avoided, are:

(a) *Underestimating the time required.* Many projects begin with aims that are too ambitious. In our moss example, for instance, many lines of investigation were possible and it was necessary to narrow these down to a single approach. A second line of investigation can always be started if the first proves inadequate.

(b) *Involving too much identification.* Surveys of whole communities should be avoided. It is better to concentrate on a few easily-identifiable groups within each of the communities under study.

(c) *Relying on equipment* that may not be available, may not work on the day or which provides measurements to a greater degree of accuracy or sophistication than is necessary. An example here would be trying to relate the distribution of a species to the overall availability of light; measurements of 'average' light conditions are very difficult to obtain and, even if you can make the measurements, their interpretation is fraught with problems.

(d) *Insufficient planning of how the data will be analysed.* It is this major and common fault that this Guide sets out to correct!

1.2   The role of statistics

One purpose of this Project Guide is to help you deal with your data. The Guide does not aim to be a course in statistics, but it does contain descriptions of several statistical techniques that are widely used, not just in ecology but also in many other disciplines both within and outside biology.

Different statistical techniques are designed to help you answer different kinds of question. They also vary in the types of data on which they can be used. For example, some can cope with only two sets of measurements, such as soil moisture values from two sites, whereas others can cope simultaneously with several. Some techniques can only be applied to measurements (such as weights, or lengths) with certain mathematical properties which are not possessed by less obviously quantitative measurements (such as flower colour). Before you start collecting your data, therefore, you have to be certain that statistical techniques are available not only to do the job that you want of them, but also to do it on the kinds of data that you intend to collect. Chapters 2 and 4 go into these issues more fully.

Many people—even many biologists—regard statistics as

an irritating formality, to be tacked on at the end of an investigation to give it an appearance of respectability. We hope to persuade you that, on the contrary, statistical techniques are there to help rather than hinder you, and that they are most effective when they are an integral part of a project rather than an unwelcome postscript.

1.3   Typical stages in a project

Many research projects go through a sequence of six activities. Look at Figure 1 which summarises them: Having made the initial observation:—

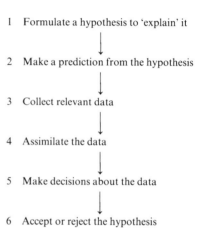

1   Formulate a hypothesis to 'explain' it

2   Make a prediction from the hypothesis

3   Collect relevant data

4   Assimilate the data

5   Make decisions about the data

6   Accept or reject the hypothesis

Figure 1.   Six stages in a typical research project.

1   The investigator formulates a hypothesis which can be tested. A typical hypothesis might be that the difference in vegetation between two apparently similar sites was caused by differences in soil moisture (or, more specifically, *field capacity*—see Section 3.5.10).

2   The investigator then makes a prediction that must follow if the hypothesis is true. For example: 'If my hypothesis is true, I shall find that the soil moisture in the two different sites is different.'

3   Next, the investigator collects data to see whether or not this prediction is true. In the present example the investigator collects soil samples from the two sites and measures their moisture values.

4   The investigator must now assimilate these data: 'What sort of measurements are turning up? How big or small are the numbers, how widely scattered are they?'

5   Then the investigator must make a decision about the data: 'Are the measurements really different in the two sites or are they more or less the same?'

6   Lastly the investigator can go back to the original hypothesis and decide whether to accept or reject it. If the soil moisture values of the soils at the two sites are the same,

then the hypothesis is false and the investigator rejects it. If the values are different, then the hypothesis stands—at least for the time being.

The most important point to grasp at this juncture is that statistical techniques can help the investigator at every one of the six stages just described. They can help you to formulate your hypothesis more precisely and to make more accurate predictions from the hypothesis. They can help you to collect data more efficiently, to display and summarise them so that they can be understood and digested more easily, and to analyse them so that you can better understand their implications for your original hypothesis. Because of this, it is important to start thinking about statistical techniques at the *beginning* of your project, and not at the very end. Sections 1.3.1–1.3.6 go through the six stages just described in more detail, to show what general principles you should think about at each stage if you are to collect and analyse your data efficiently.

1.3.1   Formulating a hypothesis

At the beginning of the project, you should think carefully about your hypothesis. In particular, you should decide

1   how specific or how general you wish it to be, and

2   to what extent you wish it to be phrased in quantitative terms.

Table 1   Three imaginary hypotheses, expressed at two different levels of generality.

(A) More general level	(B) More specific level
A1 The vegetation at sites X and Y is different because of differences in soil moisture at the two sites.	B1 The abundance of gorse (*Ulex* sp.) at sites X and Y is different because of differences in soil moisture at the two sites.
A2 The plants in this meadow grow together in clumps.	B2 The positions in which rush (*Juncus* sp.) and creeping buttercup (*Ranunculus repens*) plants grow in this meadow are not independent of one another.
A3 Pollution has affected the animal life in these streams.	B3 The abundance of the freshwater crustacean *Gammarus* varies inversely with the concentration of nitrate nitrogen in the water of these streams.

Table 1 lists three imaginary hypotheses, any one of which might reasonably form the basis of a research project. Column A of the Table phrases each hypothesis in general terms; column B in more specific terms.

The hypotheses as formulated in column B are more specific than their counterparts in A, firstly because they identify one or more specific organisms (rather than talking generally about plants or animals) and secondly because they are more explicit about the key variables that are to be investigated. Thus, hypothesis B1 makes specific mention of differences in the *abundance* of gorse in the two sites, whereas hypothesis A1 mentions only that the vegetation is 'different'. Hypothesis A2 refers only to plants that occur in clumps, whereas B2 refers specifically to the non-independence in distribution of two named species. Hypothesis A3 refers only to an unspecified effect of an unspecified pollutant, whereas B3 identifies both the animal species and the supposed pollutant, and in addition postulates a precise quantitative relationship between the abundance of one and the concentration of the other.

When you formulate the hypothesis that is to form the starting point for your own project, you are, of course, free to choose just how generally or specifically to word it, and how quantitative to make it. However, you will almost certainly do better to veer towards the more specific and the more quantitative. You will then have a clearly-formulated problem on which to work, and—most important—a good idea of what measurements you will need to collect, why you are collecting them, and what you are going to do with them once you *have* collected them. It is a common fault to start a project with only a vague idea of the hypothesis under test, and with no clear idea of what will be done with the data when they are collected. The result is that a lot of time is wasted collecting irrelevant data that are never used, whilst omitting to collect some of the information that is absolutely vital.

1.3.2   Predicting from hypotheses

A clearly formulated hypothesis will generate one or more specific predictions, which can be tested

☐   What predictions follow from the three hypotheses listed in column B of Table 1?

■   B1   The soil moisture at one of the sites is different from that at the other.

B2   If you sample several small, standard-sized areas within the meadow, then the numbers of *Juncus* and *R. repens* in each area will be found to fluctuate together. Samples containing several *Juncus* should on average contain several *R. repens,* and *vice versa.*

B3 Standard samples taken from streams with high concentrations of nitrate nitrogen will be found to contain relatively few *Gammarus,* and *vice versa.*

These predictions are fairly straightforward, and it should be easy to carry out simple projects to test them, in contrast to the hypotheses in column A of Table 1 which do not readily generate testable predictions. But, how different do the soil moisture values have to be, and to what extent must the plants fluctuate together? There are standard statistical techniques that act as yardsticks, and help you to make judgements of this kind. If you know what these techniques are at the stage of making your prediction, you can then formulate it to match a particular statistical technique.

1.3.3   Collecting data

There are three main questions that you have to answer before you collect your data:

1   *What sort of sampling should you carry out?*
For example, what techniques should you use? Should you collect data from randomly spaced areas? Should your sample areas be of a specific size—and if so, what size? Would readings taken at single points be more suitable? These questions are discussed in Sections 3.2.2. 3.2.7.

2   *How many data do you need to collect?*
For example, would five measurements of soil moisture from each site for hypothesis B1 (Table 1) be sufficient, or would 50 be needed, or 500?

☐   Intuitively, what considerations (apart from the practical ones of cost, time and the difficulty of obtaining samples) are likely to dictate the number of measurements that you need to take in order to compare the soil moisture values of the two sites effectively?

■   If the moisture values of the two sites are very different, then this difference is likely to become clear with only a few measurements from each site. However, if they are only slightly different, you may need to make many measurements from both sites before you can be convinced of the difference. Again, if the soil moisture within each site is fairly uniform, so that the measurements from each site are tightly clustered together, then any difference in moisture between the sites is likely to be revealed with fewer samples than if the moisture within each site is very variable (Figure 2).

KEY
● Soil moisture (field capacity) measurements from site 1
○ Soil moisture (field capacity) measurements from site 2
Values are g of water per 100 g of soil

(a)

(b)

(c)

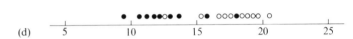
(d)

Figure 2.   Conclusions about differences between sites depend upon the distribution of data collected there.
(a) The values are very different at the two sites. This becomes clear after only a few measurements have been taken.
(b) The values are slightly different at the two sites. The difference would only emerge after many measurements had been taken.
(c) The values at each site are tightly clustered. The difference between the sites becomes clear after only a few measurements have been taken.
(d) The values at each site are widely scattered. The difference between the sites would only emerge after many measurements had been taken.

Generally speaking, where measurements are fairly uniform *within* each site, but are markedly different *between* sites, the overall difference in soil moisture will be revealed after only a few samples from each site. Where there is more variation within sites and less between sites, a larger number of measurements must be taken. The trouble is that, before you start, you may have little or no idea of the overall difference in moisture between the two sites, or of the variation within and between sites. So how do you decide, at the start of a project, how many measurements to collect? There is no simple answer to this question, and much depends upon the particular statistical technique that you are to use. For each of the techniques described in Chapter 4, we give advice on the minimum number of measurements that it is desirable for you to collect, and also on the maximum number (above which extra data collection produces diminishing returns for the effort involved). Very often in biological research, however, an investigation has to stop well short of this maximum number for such practical reasons as the time and cost involved in collecting the measurements.

One way of checking whether it is worthwhile continuing to collect data is to construct a **running mean.** Divide your readings into blocks of, say, 5 or 10 each. Take the first block and calculate the mean; then find the mean of the first two blocks together, and compare this value to the previously calculated mean. Repeat the calculation for the first three blocks, and so on. The mean values will fluctuate each time, but will gradually settle down to within closer limits, until a point is reached where adding to the sample size has only a very small effect on the mean. When this happens, you can assume that your sample size is adequate.

3 What kinds of measurement should you take?

Sometimes the type of measurement that you have to make is obvious, as in the above example. At other times, there may be several possible alternatives, and you have to decide which is best for your purposes. Take as an example hypothesis B2 in Table 1: that *Juncus* and *R. repens* are associated with each other in the meadow. One possibility would be to take a number of quadrats (see Section 3.2.2.) of standard size within the meadow, and count how many of them contained *Juncus* but not *R. repens,* how many contained *R. repens* but not *Juncus,* how many contained both, and how many contained neither. (This is, in fact, a much-used method, see Section 4.8.) You could then compare the relative numbers of these four categories with the number to be expected if the spatial distributions of *R. repens* and *Juncus* in the meadow were independent of one another.

This method has the advantage that it is fairly quick to carry out. However, it ignores a lot of useful information. For example, you would know more about how the numbers of plants of the two species fluctuated together if you counted how many of each of them occurred in each quadrat. You could then find out whether quadrats containing larger numbers of one species also contained larger numbers of the other, whether quadrats with few of one species contained few of the other, and so on. This method would obviously require you to spend more time on each quadrat but it enables you to use more effective statistical techniques on the data that you collect (see Section 4.9), so it has advantages as well as disadvantages.

Indeed, all of the statistical techniques in Chapter 4 have both advantages and disadvantages, and it is up to you to weigh them up in the context of your own project; Chapter 4 gives guidance on this. You should consider these issues at the beginning of the project, and not after it is too late to do anything about it.

1.3.4 Assimilating the data

Large chunks of data are indigestible, and it is important to use statistical techniques to summarise them in a form such that you can grasp the average magnitude of your measurements, how widely scattered they are, and how one set of measurements relates to another. There are formal statistical techniques for these purposes (see Chapter 4); but there are also some quick and simple graphical techniques (see Section 2.3) that enable you to see at a glance what kind of result you are getting. You can then make up your mind, simply by using common sense, whether they are reasonable or not. Suppose, for example, you were carrying out a project to test hypothesis B3 in Table 1, namely that the *Gammarus* abundance in several different streams varies inversely with the nitrate nitrogen concentration of the water, and that you had carried out a small-scale pilot project to establish the order of magnitude of your measurements. Let us imagine that you had taken a sample of *Gammarus* from the stream bed and a sample of the water flowing over it in each of eight different streams. You could draw a 'scattergram' (see Section 2.3.1) of your pilot

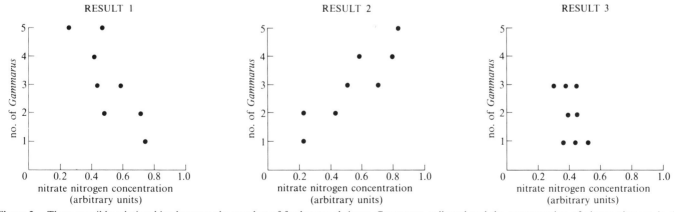

Figure 3. Three possible relationships between the number of freshwater shrimps, *Gammarus,* collected and the concentration of nitrate nitrogen in the water at eight different sites.

data, in which each point denotes the nitrate nitrogen concentration (along the horizontal axis) and the number of *Gammarus* (along the vertical axis) of your eight data points. Figure 3 illustrates three different possibilities:

RESULT 1   This looks promising, but since the numbers of *Gammarus* are rather small, you would be wise to take bigger samples.

RESULT 2   This looks intriguing. *Gammarus* seem to thrive on nitrate nitrogen. Perhaps your hypothesis is wrong at these concentrations. On the other hand, maybe your method of measuring nitrate nitrogen concentration is inaccurate, or even your method of sampling *Gammarus*. If you have used a computer to draw the scattergram, it may have done strange things to your data, so it would be worth checking the computer program.

RESULT 3   All the points are tightly clustered together here, because the range of nitrate nitrogen concentrations is so small. It means that it is impossible to deduce from the diagram whether or not variation in nitrate nitrogen concentration is associated with variation in *Gammarus* numbers. This would prompt you to look for other streams in which nitrate nitrogen concentrations varied more widely. It would also be wise to collect larger quantities of stream bed material in order to increase the *Gammarus* counts.

1.3.5   Making decisions on the basis of your data

The data that you collect should enable you to decide whether the hypothesis that you have proposed is true or false. Sometimes the data are so clear-cut that there is no difficulty in coming to such a decision. For example, if the data collected to test the three hypotheses in column B of Table 1 resembled those on the left-hand side of Figure 4, you would have no difficulty in making a decision about any of them. Unfortunately, results are rarely as clear as this. If, instead, they were as depicted on the right-hand side of Figure 4, you would probably find it quite difficult to decide unaided on the truth, or otherwise, of your hypotheses. There are, however, statistical techniques that can guide you in such situations. It is helpful to consider these techniques in relation to two broad kinds of decision that biologists often have to make:

(i)   decisions about differences.

(ii)   decisions about associations.

(i)   Decisions about differences

The aim of many research projects is to investigate whether a difference exists between two or more situations. Hypothesis B1 of Table 1, for example, requires that the experimenter investigates whether the soil moisture differs between the two sites. In this instance, the experimenter

KEY

● Soil moisture (field capacity) measurements from site 1
○ Soil moisture (field capacity) measurements from site 2
Values are g of water per 100 g of soil

B1

No. of quadrats containing:

5	*Juncus* but not *R. repens*	83
3	*R. repens* but not *Juncus*	74
150	*Juncus* and *R. repens*	78
99	neither *Juncus* nor *R. repens*	37

B2

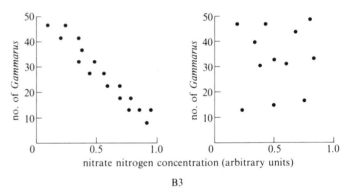

nitrate nitrogen concentration (arbitrary units)

B3

Figure 4.   The data you collect sometimes show a clear pattern (as on the left of each example) and sometimes do not (as on the right). The hypotheses were:

B1: that the difference in gorse abundance between sites 1 and 2 is due to a difference in soil moisture.

B2: that *Juncus* and *Ranunculus repens* do not grow independently of each other.

B3: that the numbers of *Gammarus* are higher when the nitrate nitrogen concentration is lower.

must choose between two incompatible alternatives: either there is a difference, or there is not. If there is a difference, the hypothesis is supported; if there is no difference, the hypothesis is false. This is perhaps the most common kind of decision made in biological research, and uses a branch of statistical theory and techniques known, appropriately enough, as **hypothesis-testing** (see Section 2.4.1).

A second kind of decision about differences that an experimenter may wish to make is 'How big is the difference?' In agricultural research, for example, an experimenter may try a new, more expensive fertilizer on a crop, and compare the yield with that from a crop grown with a standard fertilizer. The aim of the experiment would be to see whether the new fertilizer improved the yield enough to make it a commercial proposition. Statistical techniques available to provide this sort of information are described in Chapter 4.

(ii) Decisions about associations

Hypotheses B2 and B3 in Table 1 both require decisions to be made about associations: B2 requires that the experimenter decides whether there really is an association between *Juncus* and *R. repens*, B3 whether there really is a negative association between nitrate nitrogen concentration and *Gammarus* numbers. Once again, there is more than one kind of decision to be made about associations:

You may have to make a simple, yes/no decision about whether there is, or is not, an association. For example, with hypothesis B2 you would have to decide whether there was or was not an association between *R. repens* and *Juncus* in the meadow—see Chapter 4 for further details.

You may also have to make a decision about the strength of an association. Compare the two diagrams at the foot of Figure 4, which plot the number of *Gammarus* against the concentration of nitrate nitrogen in streams. The association between the two is clearly much stronger in the example on the left than in that on the right. Correlation techniques, available to tell you just how strong that association is, are described in Section 4.9.

You may wish to ask, not simply 'How strong is the association between my two sets of measurements?', but 'By how much does one of my measurements change, if the other set changes by a given amount?' For example, 'If the nitrate nitrogen concentration is doubled, how great will be the reduction in *Gammarus* abundance?' The technique that answers this kind of question is known as **regression,** and is described in Section 4.10.

1.3.6 Revisiting the hypothesis

Once you have made your decision about whether your data indicate a difference or association, or once you have decided on the size of the difference or the strength of the association, you can revisit your hypothesis and decide whether to accept or reject it. Statistical techniques will tell you how confident you can be in the decision that you have made. After comparing the two sets of soil moisture values from the two sites in B1 by a suitable technique, for example, you would be able to say: 'The probability of my

getting sets of measurements from the two sites that differ as much as these is such and such'. Not only you but also other research workers will then know how much confidence to have in your conclusions.

Always bear in mind that statistical calculations do not tell you anything directly about the *cause* of a difference or association. For instance, if you found that gorse abundance and soil moisture both differ at two sites, the real difference in the plant's performance may be due to different management practices.

Summary of Chapter 1

The most important message from this Chapter is that you should consider how you are going to collect and analyse your data right from the beginning of your project, rather than leaving these issues until later. If you know from the outset the kinds of statistical technique that are available, and the types of data that they require, this will help you to conduct each of the six stages of your project more efficiently. In particular:

1 You will be able to formulate your hypotheses in specific and quantitative terms.

2 These formulations will generate clear, testable predictions.

3 You will know roughly how many measurements to collect, and of what kind.

4 You will be able to assimilate the data easily, either by formal statistical techniques or by quick graphical methods.

5 You will be able to analyse your results formally, and so make decisions about any differences or associations that appear to exist between different sets of your measurements.

6 You will be able to make decisions about the truth or falsity of your hypotheses, and to do so with a known degree of confidence.

Objective for Chapter 1

You should be able to:

★ recognise the six different stages of a research project. Once you have developed a preliminary idea for your own project, you can test your understanding of this Objective by making sure that you can identify the six different stages in relation to it. If you have any problems over this, consult your tutor.

Chapter 2   Some basic ideas about statistical techniques

In Chapter 1, we hope that we convinced you that statistical techniques can help you at every stage of your project. We now need to introduce some ideas that are fundamental to the kinds of statistical analysis that you will need to carry out in your research. You should, therefore, master the information in this chapter, and make sure that you have achieved the Objectives set out at the end of it before you start on Chapter 4.

The four questions dealt with in Chapter 2 are:

1   What exactly are samples, and what information do they provide?

2   What sorts of measurements can you take, and what can you do with them?

3   How do you display and summarise data?

4   What do you do when you carry out statistical tests?

2.1   Sampling

It is usually only possible to collect a limited amount of data during the course of your project. In the three projects listed in Table 1, for example, you might have time to take, perhaps, 20 soil moisture measurements from each of the two sites, or to count the numbers of *Juncus* and *R. repens* in, say, 70 quadrats, or to take samples from 10 streams. It is not usually practicable to take a complete set of measurements: to measure soil moisture at every point in the two sites, to consider every small area of an entire meadow, or to collect water from all the streams. Despite the limited number of measurements that you collect, you hope that they will tell you something about the situation in general: that the 20 measurements from the two sites will tell you something about what the moisture at the two sites as a whole is really like, that the 70 quadrats will give a good idea of the association of *Juncus* and *R. repens* in the meadow as a whole, and that the 10 pairs of samples will give a good idea of the relationship between the concentration of nitrate nitrogen and the numbers of *Gammarus*.

Two terms are used to describe respectively:

(i)   The limited collection of measurements that you make—this is the **sample**;

(ii)   The larger collection of measurements that are potentially available for you to take, and of which you hope that your sample will be representative—this is the **population**.

Figure 5 should make these two terms clear.

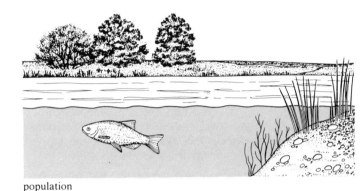

population

sample

Figure 5.   The difference between a statistical sample and a statistical population. In this case, the bottles of water you collect constitute the statistical sample. All the water that could be sampled constitutes the population. (The fish is there only to indicate water!)

Note that the terms sample and population have these special meanings in statistics. It is unfortunate that they have rather different meanings in biology. Thus, in example B1 of Table 1, you may collect a piece of soil from one of the two sites, and call it a sample. In statistical terminology, by contrast, it is the collection of 20 soil moisture measurements from the site that constitutes the sample, not the individual piece of soil from which you take a single measurement. Because there are 20 measurements in the sample, the **sample size** is said to be 20.

The term population, too, has a specialised meaning in biology, indicating the breeding group to which an individual belongs, which is different from the statistical meaning given above.

Much biological research consists of taking measurements from samples of manageable size, in order to gain information about the unmanageably large populations from which the samples originate. In other words, we make **inferences** about the population from the properties of samples taken from that population. Several of the statistical techniques described in Chapter 4 tell us how confident we can be in drawing certain inferences in given situations.

2.2 Measurements

2.2.1 Levels of measurements

Biologists take different kinds of measurement. The difference that concerns us here is not that some people measure pH, others height, others animal numbers, and so on, but rather that measurements can vary in their quantitative nature. To use the formal terminology, there are different **levels of measurement.** Three different levels are relevant to us here: **interval, ordinal** and **categorical** (or **nominal**).

(a) *Interval level measurements*

These are what you might think of as 'real' measurements, like height, weight, and so on. The distinguishing feature of this level of measurement is that you can assess the size of the differences between measurements. For example, if there are three plants, respectively 18, 12 and 9 cm high, then you can say not only that the difference in height between the first two is 6 cm, but that this difference is twice as large as the difference between the 12 cm and 9 cm plants.

(b) *Ordinal level measurements*

These are measurements where it is possible to say that one is bigger than another, and so to rank them with respect to each other, but it is impossible to assess the size of the differences. For example, you may be able to assess the extent of fungal infestation of a crop using the following rating scale:

1	no infestation	4	heavy infestation
2	slight infestation	5	severe infestation
3	moderate infestation		

It may be impossible to quantify the infestation more precisely than this, but nonetheless possible to assign confidently a crop under investigation to one or other of these categories. Hence, one could rank different samples of the crop, and say that a sample with grade 4 infestation was more severely infested than one with a grade 2 infestation. It would not be meaningful, however, to say that a grade 4 infestation was twice as heavy as a grade 2 or four times as heavy as a grade 1. Hence, this is measurement at the 'ordinal' level, because one can do no more than rank the measurements in order. Other examples of ordinal levels of measurement would include subjective ratings of:

The degree of camouflage achieved by a prey species at different points in its habitat;

The degree of 'open-ness' or 'shelter' afforded by a habitat; The intensity of the scent emitted by a flower, when assessed using your sense of smell.

(c) *Categorical (or nominal) level measurements*

These are measurements where you can do no more than say that the object measured belongs to this or that particular category. There is no sense in which you can arrange the categories in an order, such that one category ranks higher than another. In this respect categorical level measurements differ from ordinal ones. In example B2 in Table 1, the section of meadow enclosed by a quadrat might be identified as belonging to one of four categories: (i) containing *Juncus* but not *R. repens*; (ii) containing *R. repens* but not *Juncus*; (iii) containing both *Juncus* and *R. repens*; (iv) containing neither *Juncus* nor *R. repens*. If several 1 m² areas within the meadow are classified in this way, then one builds up a record of how many of the areas fall into each of the four categories.

Other examples of categorical measurements include:

identifying each animal of a given species as either male or female (hence counting the relative numbers of males and females in the sample);

identifying a host as parasitised or unparasitised (hence counting the relative numbers of parasitised and unparasitised individuals in the sample).

The reason for stressing these three different levels of measurement is that some of the statistical techniques described in Chapter 4 are suited to one level of measurement, whereas others are suited to another. You therefore have to be certain, before you use a technique, which level your measurements are at, and which techniques can be applied to them.

2.2.2 Matched and unmatched measurements

Many research projects, like those required to test hypotheses B1 and B3 in Table 1, involve an analysis of two samples: that is, two sets of measurements. In example B1, these are two sets of soil moisture measurements, in B3 they are a set of *Gammarus* numbers and a set of nitrate nitrogen concentrations. You have to decide whether these measurements can be **matched** together in pairs or not, because some of the techniques described in Chapter 4 can only be applied to matched pairs of measurements, whereas others are to be used on unmatched sets. By 'matched pairs', we mean that one measurement from one of the samples can be paired with one and only one measurement from the other sample. In B3 for example, each measurement of *Gammarus* numbers obtained from each stream bed site must be matched with the particular nitrate nitrogen concentration measured in the water taken from that site. Hence, the measurements can be arranged in matched pairs, which is just what we need to investigate the association between *Gammarus* abundance and nitrate nitrogen concentration.

As another example, you may wish to investigate the extent to which the tendency of a species of butterfly to settle on a patch of ground depends upon the sunlight falling on that patch. You could then select a number of patches of ground and count (for each one) how many butterflies settled there per hour when the sun was shining, and how many when the sky was overcast. For each patch of ground you would, therefore, have a matched pair of measurements, one for sunny conditions and one for overcast. By contrast, the experiment needed to test hypothesis B1 in Table 1 would be carried out on unmatched measurements. You would take, say, 20 soil moisture measurements from each of the two sites, but there would probably be no particular reason for pairing any one measurement from site x with any one measurement from site y.

In many research projects, you have little choice over whether the measurements are to be matched or not: the nature of the project itself dictates whether or not the measurements will be paired. Sometimes, however, the choice *is* under your control. In the butterfly example, you could either have chosen to count butterflies on each patch of ground under two different conditions, so obtaining matched measurements, or you could have chosen to look at two completely different sets of patches of ground, one under sunny and the other under overcast conditions. Generally speaking, when the option is open to you, it is better to collect your data as matched rather than unmatched pairs. The reason for this can again be seen from the butterfly example. Different patches of ground may vary in their attractiveness to butterflies, regardless of the weather conditions: some may attract dozens of butterflies, others virtually none. In Figure 6, for example, patch 2 always attracts more butterflies than patch 1—even when patch 1 is in the sun and patch 2 in the shade. This variability will tend to obscure any effects of the sun on patch-visiting by butterflies. However, if you collect a matched pair of measurements from each patch, one under sunny and the other under overcast conditions, you can overcome this problem by comparing your measurements *within* each pair and seeing how big a difference the change in conditions makes to each patch. Figure 6 shows that in both patches 1 and 2, an average of two more butterflies per hour visit during sunny conditions than visit during overcast conditions.

2.3   Displaying and summarising data

2.3.1   Lineplots, histograms and scattergrams

Once you have collected your measurements, you will want

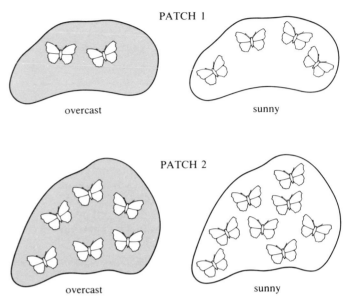

Figure 6.   The average number of butterflies visiting two patches of ground under different conditions.

to get a rough idea of what they are like as soon as possible—especially how large they are and how widely scattered. A quick and useful device, particularly for small samples, is called a **lineplot.** Suppose that you are collecting interval level data, such as weights of leaves, and that your 12 measurements are as listed at the top of Figure 7. To make a lineplot, draw a horizontal line with a scale on it and indicate, with a dot, where along the line each measurement falls—as in Figure 7(a). If more than one measurement has the same value, simply arrange the relevant dots vertically above one another.

With larger samples of interval level data it is useful to construct a **histogram.** Here, you decide upon certain ranges of measurements and count how many of your measurements fall into each range. You could, for example, display the leaf weights of Figure 7 as a histogram. You could choose to count how many leaves fell into the weight ranges 0–1·9, 2–3·9, 4–5·9, 6–7·9, 8–9·9 and 10–11·9 grams—see Figure 7(b). You could then depict this by putting the ranges you have chosen along the horizontal axis and the number of measurements in each range along the vertical axis— see Figure 7(c).

Lineplots and histograms are useful precisely because they are so simple, and thus give you a direct, common sense idea of what your data are like. You can use them to check the results of more sophisticated statistical analyses that you perform subsequently on your data. If these analyses give results that seem to be at odds with your lineplots (for example, by suggesting that two samples are different when your lineplots indicate that they are not, or *vice versa*), then

weight of leaves/g:

| 7.2 | 4.9 | 7.2 | 10.6 | 8.4 | 9.2 |
| 5.3 | 6.8 | 5.0 | 5.7 | 6.1 | 5.0 |

(a)

(b)

0–1.9	2–3.9	4–5.9	6–7.9	8–9.9	10–11.9	weight range/g
0	0	5	4	2	1	no. of leaves within each range

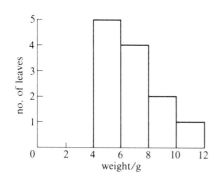

(c)

Figure 7. Displaying your data: (a) a **lineplot** of leaf weights. (b) a **grouping** of the same leaf weights into ranges. (c) the same information plotted as a **histogram**.

you need to check those analyses very carefully to see whether they have been correctly carried out.

The idea of a lineplot can be extended to cope with two rather than one set of measurements from your sample. In B3 of Table 1, for example, where you have both *Gammarus* counts and nitrate nitrogen concentrations, you can draw two scales, one for each measurement, at right angles to one another, and put a dot in the appropriate place for each pair of measurements (as in the diagrams at the foot of Figure 4). Thus, in the left-hand diagram, the top left-hand point corresponds to a water sample with a nitrate nitrogen concentration of about 0·1 and an associated *Gammarus* concentration of about 45. This form of pictorial display is called a **scattergram** (or **scatter diagram**), and gives a preliminary idea as to whether the two sets of measurements are or are not associated with one another.

Once you have gained an initial impression about your data, you will almost certainly need to obtain more precise information about them. In particular, you will wish to know their average value and how widely scattered they are.

2.3.2 Sample averages

You are probably already familiar with the idea of the **mean** (or, more strictly, the **arithmetical mean**) as a measure of an **average** value. Briefly, the mean of a sample is the sum of the measurements divided by the number of measurements (that is, by the sample size).

☐ Six water temperature readings are taken, as follows: 15·3, 17·8, 13·2, 14·0, 19·9 and 14·9°C.

Calculate their mean.

■ mean = (sum) ÷ (sample size)

$$= \frac{15·3 + 17·8 + 13·2 + 14·0 + 19·9 + 14·9}{6}$$

$$= 15·85$$

Notice the convention that the mean is quoted to one more significant figure than the individual measurements from which it was calculated.

The symbols that people use to denote the mean and the sample size vary, but we shall use the following widely adopted conventions:

An individual *measurement* from a sample is denoted by an italic lower case letter, such as x or t (x is very commonly used; t is sometimes used if the measurements are times—but, if you use t, beware of confusion with the test statistic t (Section 4.5)).

The *mean* of a sample is denoted by an italic lower case letter with a horizontal line on top, for example $\bar{x}$ or $\bar{t}$ (pronounced x bar or t bar).

The sample *size* is denoted by the italic lower case letter n.

The instruction 'sum the numbers' (or 'add all the numbers together') is denoted by the Greek capital letter sigma Σ.

Hence, using this terminology the equation

mean = (sum) ÷ (sample size)

becomes

$$\bar{x} = \frac{(\Sigma x)}{n}$$

or, if you are using the letter t,

$$\bar{t} = \frac{(\Sigma t)}{n}$$

Another important measure of the average size of the measurements of a sample is the **median**. This is the value

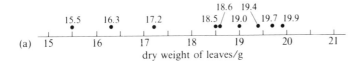

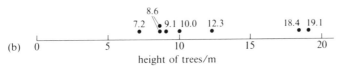

Figure 8. Finding the median: (a) the dry weights of nine batches of dandelion leaves. (b) the heights of eight sycamore trees.

above which half of the measurements in the sample lie, and below which the other half lie.

The median is especially easy to work out if you have already displayed your measurements in a lineplot. Look at Figure 8(a), which shows nine dry weight measurements of dandelion leaves arranged in the form of a lineplot. The median of this sample is 18·6, because there are just as many measurements below 18·6 as there are above it. Now look at Figure 8(b) which shows the heights of eight sycamore trees. Because the sample size is an even number (8) there is no single measurement that has half of the others above and half below it. When the sample size is an even number, therefore, you take the *pair* of measurements that have half of the measurements above and half below them. In this example they are 9·1 and 10·0. The median for the sample lies half way between these two numbers; that is, at 9·55. (A simple way of calculating the required number is to add the two measurements together and then divide by two. In this example, 9·1 + 10·0 = 19·1; then 19·1 ÷ 2 = 9·55.)

Notice also from Figure 8(b) that it does not matter that two of the measurements have the same value, 8·6. They are still counted as separate measurements.

☐ Calculate the sample means for each of the two sets of data in Figure 8. How do they compare with the sample medians?

■ The mean for the sample in Figure 8(a) is 18·23, and for the sample in Figure 8(b) it is 11·66. The median for the first sample is 18·6, which is slightly higher than the mean of 18·23. The median for the second sample is 9·55, which is rather lower than the mean of 11·66.

The reason for these differences between the means and medians is that, in both instances, the measurements are clustered towards one end of the scale: they are what is called **skewed**. The sample mean is calculated from every measurement in the sample, and so the few extreme measurements at the 'thinly populated' end of the scale

affect the sample mean by pulling it towards that end. The sample median, by contrast, is not affected by the precise values of the extreme measurements. For example, if the highest measurement in Figure 8(a) were 19·9 million instead of 19·9, the sample median would still be 18·6 (whereas the sample mean would be 2, 211, 127·13).

Medians are often useful, therefore, where measurements appear to have a skewed distribution. However, as Chapter 4 explains, the kinds of statistical techniques that can be applied to medians are different from those that can be applied to means.

A final point to note is that throughout this Section we have referred to *sample* means and *sample* medians. The word 'sample' is emphasized here, because we can also talk about *population* means and *population* medians. The difference is important (Section 2.4).

2.3.3 The scatter of measurements within a sample

Whenever you collect a set of biological measurements that make up a sample, you will find that they vary from one measurement to another. This is a characteristic of biological material, and is a reflection of the multitude of factors that can affect the precise value of any particular feature such as height, weight or abundance. Look at Figure 9 which gives the wing lengths in three samples of moths as lineplots. The sample mean is the same in each of these three cases, 12·92 mm, but the extent to which the measurements are scattered around the mean value is different in each case.

☐ Summarise the differences.

■ The measurements are more tightly clustered around the sample mean in sample 2 than in samples 1 or 3. They are more evenly scattered in samples 1 and 2 than in 3: in sample 3 most of the measurements are clustered tightly round the sample mean, but the two most

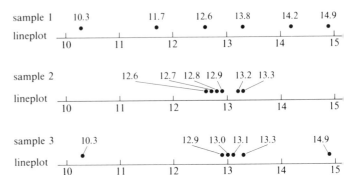

Figure 9. Lineplots of wing length for three hypothetical samples of moths. The mean is the same in each case—12·92 mm—but the scatter is very different.

extreme measurements are as far from the sample mean as their counterparts are in sample 1.

It is useful to have a way of indicating the extent to which measurements are scattered: a technique that will produce a number which will be bigger the more widely the measurements are scattered. Two such techniques are likely to be useful to you, one quick and easy, the other slightly more time-consuming, but more informative.

1 *The sample range*   This is simply the distance between the highest and lowest measurements in the sample:

sample range = (highest measurement) − (lowest measurement)

☐ Calculate the ranges for the three samples in Figure 9.

■ They are:

Sample 1: $14.9 - 10.3 = 4.6$ mm

Sample 2: $13.3 - 12.6 = 0.7$ mm

Sample 3: $14.9 - 10.3 = 4.6$ mm

Notice that the ranges of samples 1 and 3 are much bigger than that of sample 2, which is in line with the smaller degree of scatter in sample 2. Notice also, however, that the ranges for samples 1 and 3 are identical, although most of the measurements in sample 3 are not so widely scattered as those in sample 1. The range has, in this instance, failed to pick up an important difference between samples 1 and 3. This is because it concentrates solely on the highest and lowest measurements in each sample, and ignores all the others. This disadvantage does not occur with the second measure of scatter:—

2 *The sample standard deviation*   The idea behind a **standard deviation** of a sample, s, is to find a sort of average distance of your measurements from the sample mean. If you were literally to calculate this average distance you would discover that it was always zero. For example a sample of three measurements, 5 mm, 6 mm and 7 mm respectively, has a sample mean of 6.0 mm, and deviations from this mean of -1.0, 0 and $+1.0$ mm respectively. The average of these deviations is 0:

$$\frac{-1.0 + 0 + 1.0}{3} = 0$$

To overcome this problem, it is necessary to square the deviations of the measurements from the mean; this gets rid of the minus signs:

$$-1.0^2 = 1.0 \qquad 0.0^2 = 0.0 \qquad 1.0^2 = 1.0$$

Then you could take the average of the deviations squared:

$$\frac{1.0 + 0.0 + 1.0}{3} = 0.67$$

In fact, it is usual to introduce another slight complication in finding this average; rather than dividing by the sample

size, you divide by *one less* than the sample size. Here the sample size is 3, so you divide by $(3 - 1) = 2$:

$$\frac{1.0 + 0.0 + 1.0}{2} = 1.0 \text{ [This figure is called the } \textbf{variance } (s^2), \text{ see p. 15]}$$

Then take the square root to return you to the original units of measurement. (If your original measurements are in millimetres, then your sample standard deviation is also in millimetres. Note, then, that when you quote a standard deviation you should always give the units in which it is measured.) So, the standard deviation of the sample is:

$$s = \sqrt{1.0} = 1.0 \text{ mm}$$

We can put this procedure for calculating the sample standard deviation into symbols. If the standard deviation of a sample is denoted by s, the sample mean by $\bar{x}$, the sample size by n, and each measurement in the sample by x, then s is calculated from the equation:

$$s = \sqrt{\frac{\Sigma(x - \bar{x})^2}{n - 1}} \qquad (1)$$

To put this equation into practice, you proceed as follows:

 (i) Calculate the sample mean, $\bar{x}$.

(ii) Subtract the sample mean from each measurement in the sample and square the result:

$$(x - \bar{x})^2$$

(iii) Add together all of the numbers you have calculated in (ii):

$$\Sigma(x - \bar{x})^2$$

(iv) Divide the figure obtained in (iii) by one less than the sample size, $n - 1$

$$\frac{\Sigma(x - \bar{x})^2}{n - 1}$$

(v) Take the square root of the number calculated in (iv):

$$s = \sqrt{\frac{\Sigma(x - \bar{x})^2}{n - 1}}$$

Many calculators and computers have programs for calculating standard deviations of samples directly from original sample measurements. (Sometimes these are referred to as 'standard deviations with an $n - 1$ weighting' to distinguish them from another kind of standard deviation). If you have to calculate the standard deviation of a sample without such help, equation 1 is tedious to use. A quicker method which leads to the same result uses:—

$$s = \sqrt{\frac{\Sigma x^2 - (\Sigma x)^2/n}{n - 1}} \qquad (2)$$

There follows a worked example using equation 2, to calculate the standard deviations of the moth wing length samples from Figure 9.

WORKED EXAMPLE
Procedure

Calculation

1   Write down all of the measurements in sample 1 in a single column, and beside each figure write its square.

wing length, x/mm	x^2/mm^2
10·3	106·09
11·7	136·89
12·6	158·76
13·8	190·44
14·2	201·64
14·9	222·01

2   Add up the numbers in each column, giving Σx and Σx^2 respectively.

total : $\Sigma x =$ 77·5   total: $\Sigma x^2 = 1015\cdot 83$

3   Divide the total of the measurements by the sample size n. This gives $(\Sigma x)/n$ (which is the sample mean $\bar{x}$).

$$\frac{\Sigma x}{n} = \frac{77\cdot 5}{6}$$
$$= 12\cdot 9167$$
$$\bar{x} = 12\cdot 9167$$

4   Square the total of the measurements to give $(\Sigma x)^2$.

$(\Sigma x)^2 = 77\cdot 5^2$
$= 6006\cdot 25$

5   Divide the number calculated in step 4 by n to give $(\Sigma x)^2/n$.

$(\Sigma x)^2/n = 6006\cdot 25/6$
$= 1001\cdot 04$

6   Subtract $(\Sigma x)^2/n$ from the total of the squared measurements to give $\Sigma x^2 - (\Sigma x)^2/n$.

$\Sigma x^2 - (\Sigma x)^2/n = 1015\cdot 83 - 1001\cdot 04$
$= 14\cdot 79$

7   Divide the number calculated in step 6 by $n-1$ (This is the variance, s^2).

$$s^2 = \frac{\Sigma x^2 - (\Sigma x)^2/n}{n-1} = \frac{14\cdot 79}{5}$$
$$= 2\cdot 958$$

8   Take the square root of the number calculated in step 7 (This is s).

$$s = \sqrt{\frac{\Sigma x^2 - (\Sigma x)^2/n}{n-1}} = 1\cdot 71988$$

9   To complete the calculation, round the sample mean and the sample standard deviation to the same number of decimal places and write in the units of measurement.

$\bar{x} = 12\cdot 92$ mm
$s = 1\cdot 72$ mm

The standard deviations of samples 2 and 3 can be calculated in the same way. Table 2 gives the results.

Table 2   Sample standard deviations of moth wing lengths from the three samples shown in Figure 9.

	standard deviation
sample 1	1·72 mm
sample 2	0·28 mm
sample 3	1·48 mm

Notice that the standard deviation of sample 2 is smaller than that of the other two samples. Referring back to Figure 9, this is as it should be. Notice also that the standard deviation of sample 3 is smaller than that of sample 1, reflecting the greater clustering of the points around the mean in sample 3, even though the ranges of the two samples are identical. Hence, the sample standard deviation is a more sensitive measure of scatter than the range.

There are two further points to be mentioned in connection with the sample standard deviation, s. First, the final stage in the calculation of s is to take the square root of a number,

$$\text{either} \quad s = \sqrt{\frac{\Sigma(x - \overline{x})^2}{n - 1}} \quad \text{or} \quad s = \sqrt{\frac{\Sigma x^2 - (\Sigma x)^2}{n - 1}}$$

depending upon which equation you are using. If you omit this final stage, you will have calculated the square of the sample standard deviation,

$$\text{either} \quad s^2 = \frac{\Sigma(x - \overline{x})^2}{n - 1} \quad \text{or} \quad s^2 = \frac{\Sigma x^2 - (\Sigma x)^2/n}{n - 1}$$

This quantity s^2, which is known as the **sample variance,** is very important in statistics as you will see later, and it figures prominently in several of the techniques described in Chapter 4.

Second, you may be wondering why the calculation of the sample variance and the sample standard deviation are calculated by dividing by $(n-1)$ rather than by n. Theoretically, you could use either $(n-1)$ or n as the divisor; a discussion of when it would be appropriate to use one, rather than the other, is beyond the scope of this book. We advise that you use $(n-1)$ throughout unless you have sufficient knowledge of statistics to judge whether this would be less appropriate than using n.

We have now discussed the sample mean, sample median, sample range, sample standard deviation and sample variance. Each of these is a single number that represents some property of the sample from which it is calculated. The general term given to cover any such number calculated from a sample is **sample statistic.** Thus, the sample mean is a particular instance of a sample statistic, and so on.

To summarise, when you are collecting measurements, particularly on an interval scale of measurement, you should make a quick initial impression about them by drawing a lineplot or histogram. You should calculate the sample mean, or if the sample is noticeably skewed, the sample median. You should also note the range, and calculate the sample standard deviation to give you an idea of how scattered your measurements are.

2.3.4 Measurements and rounding

The calculation of the sample mean and the sample standard deviation are examples of instances where the researcher has to carry out arithmetic manipulations on the data. If you use a calculator, you will find that it gives the answer at each stage in the calculation to many significant figures. It is tempting to simplify calculations by rounding off the numbers to, say, four significant figures. In the

worked example above, for example, it might seem sensible to simplify the sum of the squared measurements to 1016 instead of using the more accurate value of 1015·83, given by the calculator, throughout the calculations.

It is important, however, not to round off numbers too early in a calculation, because the slight errors that result may become greatly magnified as your calculation proceeds. We recommend, therefore, that you work through a calculation to the maximum accuracy possible with your calculator. Only at the end, when you have your final result, should you round it to an accuracy appropriate to the kind of measurement you are taking. In the Project Guide, we have worked out our calculations to six significant figures, and have then given the final answer to one more significant figure than the original measurements.

2.4 Statistical inference

A major feature of biological research is that one uses data from samples of finite, and often rather small, size to make inferences about the populations from which they come (Section 2.1). Section 1.3.5(i) mentions two kinds of inference that biologists commonly wish to make. They are: (a) whether there is a difference in a particular feature between two populations, and (b) how big such a difference might be. The methods used to answer these questions are called hypothesis-testing and estimation techniques, respectively. Section 2.4.1 describes the principles on which hypothesis testing is based. Estimation techniques are considered in Section 2.4.2.

2.4.1 Hypothesis testing

All **hypothesis testing** proceeds through a standard sequence of reasoning. Take hypothesis B1 in Table 1, which is concerned with whether or not the soil moisture values of soils from two sites are different. The chain of reasoning is as follows:

(a) Assume, for the moment, that the averages of the soil moisture values from the two sites are the same.

(b) Take several measurements of soil moisture at each site and see whether the values from the two sites are, on the whole, close to each other or far apart.

(c) Assess the probability of getting moisture values at least as far apart as those you have obtained, if the two sites do not actually differ in overall moisture content.

(d) If this probability is too low, reject the assumption made in (a) and accept that the mean soil moisture values at the two sites are different.

This is a specific example, of course, but the same four-step chain of reasoning applies generally across the whole field of hypothesis testing. Put in more general terms, and refining some ideas slightly, the steps in the argument are as follows:

1   *Formulate a hypothesis that no difference exists in the specified feature, in the populations from which the two samples are taken*

COMMENTS

(i) Such a hypothesis of 'no difference' is called a **null hypothesis**. It is usually denoted by the symbol H_0. Note particularly that the null hypothesis refers to the *populations* from which the samples are taken, and not to the samples themselves.

(ii) Note also that the null hypothesis refers to a *specified feature* of the populations. Most often the null hypothesis refers to the **population means** of the measurements in question: that is, the null hypothesis states that the samples come from populations that do not differ in their means (for whatever feature is being measured). Another feature commonly specified in a null hypothesis is the **population median**: that is, the null hypothesis states that the samples come from populations that do not differ in their medians. A third feature that you may well wish to specify in a null hypothesis is the **population variance**: that is, the null hypothesis states that the samples come from populations that do not differ in their variances. Which of these features you should specify varies from one situation to another. Chapter 4 contains advice on how to decide on the most appropriate feature for a given situation.

(iii) In competition with the null hypothesis, as it were, you have to formulate an **alternative hypothesis**. This must be worded in such a way that if the null hypothesis is true then the alternative hypothesis is false, and vice versa. The simplest form of alternative hypothesis is the direct converse of the null hypothesis. Thus, if the null hypothesis states that no difference exists between the population means, then the alternative hypothesis states that a difference *does* exist. The symbol used to denote the alternative hypothesis is H_1.

(iv) The null and alternative hypotheses need not be limited just to two populations. It would be perfectly possible, for example, to compare the soil moisture values from, say, five sites, and formulate a null hypothesis that the mean soil moisture did not differ between the sites.

2   *Look at the measurements obtained for the samples from the populations*

Remember from Section 1.3.4 that if the measurements within samples are tightly clustered, and if the measurements for different samples are very different in magnitude, then we may be confident that the samples came from different populations. However, the greater the scatter of measurements *within* the samples and the smaller the difference in measurements *between* samples, the less confident we can be that such a difference exists. This statement can be re-phrased using the terminology of Section 2.4, namely: a null hypothesis of no difference in population means or medians is the more likely to be rejected, the bigger the difference in sample means or medians and the smaller the scatter of measurements within each sample.

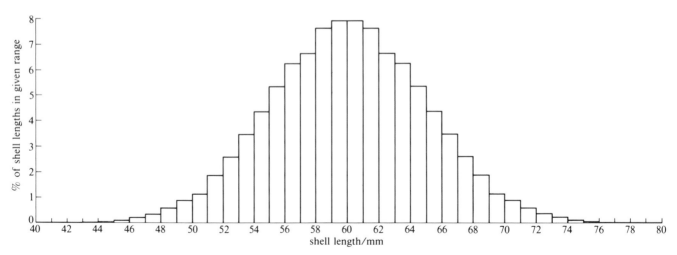

Figure 10.   An example of the normal distribution: a length/frequency plot for a hypothetical marine mollusc—the crampon.

[Note that, in order to give a plot of this form, the crampon must be an annual species, with a single short breeding season—and must either be hermaphrodite or show no sexual differences in shell growth or form

3 *Work out the probability under the null hypothesis of obtaining measurements at least as far apart as the ones you have collected*

The techniques for working out a probability under a null hypothesis can be complicated. Fortunately, the hard work has already been done by statisticians, and Tables exist from which you can read off the required probability, provided you understand certain principles. These are perhaps more readily explained with reference to an example, so we shall consider a hypothetical set of measurements on an imaginary marine snail called *Crampon maritimus*.

Imagine that it were possible to measure the shell length of every single crampon living around the British Isles. It would then be possible to find out how many shells lay between, say, 40 and 41 mm in length, how many between 41 and 42 mm, and so on up to the very top of the range of lengths. Rather than expressing these as actual numbers, you could equally well express them as percentages of all the shells counted. This has been done in Figure 10, which shows the percentage of all the crampon shells between 40 and 41 mm long, and so on. The shell lengths summarised in this Figure constitute, in the statistical sense of the word, a population. In reality it would be impossible to measure the entire population of any marine snail; but one tiny fraction of the population of measurements might give the data listed in Table 3.

Notice from Figure 10 that most of the shells are about 60 mm long, that the further from the mean value of 60 mm one goes the fewer individuals there are, and that the measurements fall symmetrically around the mean value. These characteristics are typical of certain biological measurements, and the shape of the distribution of

Table 3 Shell lengths of 100 crampons. For this sample, mean shell length ($\bar{x}$) = 60·45 mm, and sample standard deviation (s) = 5·04 mm.

sample measurements/mm

60·6	66·8	59·7	71·7	60·6	71·9	57·8	61·9	63·6	69·9
67·0	57·5	57·0	58·7	61·8	55·6	60·4	62·5	53·9	56·2
60·3	55·8	61·8	58·2	55·3	54·2	60·1	59·8	50·5	55·3
59·9	67·5	57·7	56·0	63·6	55·5	58·6	59·7	59·0	72·1
63·9	61·0	65·6	60·8	50·8	55·5	57·7	61·5	64·1	71·1
59·4	53·0	61·9	54·2	62·4	55·5	54·4	63·1	57·8	67·2
62·1	62·5	54·4	57·5	56·6	55·7	61·4	67·3	56·3	64·6
58·5	62·1	71·1	55·8	71·0	62·4	61·9	68·6	63·4	55·8
56·6	53·2	60·1	62·8	63·1	65·3	64·8	60·6	67·7	54·7
52·6	58·6	59·6	57·4	64·3	56·7	54·0	56·5	68·1	62·5

measurements in Figure 10 is known as the **normal distribution.**

4 *Decide whether to reject the null hypothesis*

If somebody brought you a crampon of unknown origin measuring, say, 62·5 mm and asked you whether you thought it could possibly have come from the British Isles on the basis of its shell length, you would have little hesitation in saying that it could. This shell is only 2·05 mm different in length from the mean of 60·45 mm, and Figure 10 shows that shells differing from the population mean by this amount (or more) are relatively common around Britain. If, however, someone brought you instead a shell 74·2 mm long, you might be doubtful: this shell is nearly 14 mm from the mean. Figure 10 shows that as few as 0·2% of crampon shells are more than 14 mm from the mean. If, finally, you were shown a shell 92·8 mm long, you would say that almost certainly it did not come from the British crampon population, because virtually no British shells are as far as this from the mean.

Your decision in each of these three instances is determined by your knowledge of the probability of obtaining measurements more than various distances from the mean. You say, in effect, 'What is the probability of obtaining a shell from the British population *at least* as far from the mean as this?' If the probability is sufficiently small, you say that the shell is very unlikely to have come from the British population.

You may wonder how one can work out the probabilities concerned. Where, in other words, do the percentages of Figure 10 come from? The answer lies in the normal distribution. The normal distribution has certain key properties. In particular, approximately 33% of the measurements in the population lie more than one standard deviation from the mean, and approximately 5% more than two standard deviations from the mean. In fact, it is possible to work out what percentage of measurements lie further than any particular number of standard deviations from the mean, whether it be 1, 2, 1·5, 0·36 standard deviations or whatever. It is because we know the properties of the normal distribution exactly that we are able to calculate the probability of obtaining a given measurement that differs by more than x standard deviations from the mean, where x is any number we choose.

A similar kind of reasoning to that used above would apply if somebody brought you, not one, but a sample of several shells and asked you if they could have come from the British population. This is equivalent to setting up a null hypothesis that there is no difference between the mean shell length of the British population and the mean shell length of the population from which the sample came. To illustrate this reasoning, imagine that the sample size were 5, and were to come from the collection of measurements in Table 3. Select five measurements from this Table at random, by using Table III(1) in Appendix III—a Random Numbers Table—as follows. Select any two-digit number from that Table with a pin. Suppose the number you choose is 78 (from row 4, column 1). Now refer to the measurements in Table 3 and choose row 7 and column 8, that is 67·3 mm. Choose the other four measurements in a similar way. Calculate the mean and the median for the five measurements you have selected. Repeat the whole process for two other samples, each containing five measurements. You will thus end up with three samples of five measurements each, together with three sample means and three sample medians.

☐ How do your sample means compare with each other and with the population mean?

Table 4   The means of 50 shell-length samples, each containing five measurements, taken from the population of British crampons, part of which is shown in Table 3. The mean of the 50 sample means $(\overline{x}) = 59\cdot740$ mm, and the standard deviation of the 50 sample means $(s) = 1\cdot829$ mm.

sample means/mm				
59·85	57·36	58·76	61·22	61·21
62·40	59·67	57·23	57·65	62·00
59·08	60·27	58·73	59·27	56·88
60·32	60·23	62·13	61·50	59·96
58·05	56·99	56·84	61·03	60·17
60·26	60·84	63·96	60·69	59·76
58·40	60·83	59·38	59·58	58·96
59·16	62·27	57·32	58·59	59·96
62·40	58·28	57·51	57·51	59·27
60·35	65·13	58·45	58·81	60·51

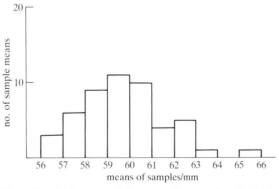

Figure 11.   A histogram of the 50 sample means from Table 4.

■ Your sample means are very likely to be close together but slightly different from one another: it is extremely unlikely that they will be exactly the same. The sample means are also likely to be close to the population mean of 60·45 mm.

The sample medians are also likely to be similar to each other but not identical. This exercise demonstrates an important feature of samples: if you take many samples from a population, and calculate the sample means or medians, they will vary from one sample to another. Just as it is possible to draw a frequency distribution of the individual measurements that make up a sample, so it is possible to draw a frequency distribution of the sample means or medians. For example, Table 4 shows the respective means of 50 samples (each containing five measurements) taken from the population of British crampons. Figure 11 is a histogram of these means. Notice three things about this histogram:

(i) The means are themselves clustered around a mean value. In this instance, the mean value is 59·74 mm, which, by no coincidence, is very close to the population mean of 60·45 mm.

(ii) The means appear to be normally distributed, and we ask you to take it on trust that they are, in fact, normally distributed. The significance of this is that we can therefore work out the probability that a given sample mean will be more than a certain distance from the mean of the sample means, just as we did earlier for the original measurements.

(iii) The sample means are more tightly clustered around their mean than are the original measurements around *their* mean. (Compare Figure 11, which shows that virtually all of the sample means lie between 55 and 65 mm, with Figure 10 which shows that many of the original measurements lie outside these values.)

In fact, it is perfectly possible to calculate a standard deviation for the sample means, to discover just how scattered they are. This turns out to be 1·829 mm. The standard deviation of the original measurements, by contrast, is 5·04 mm.

The standard deviation of a sample statistic such as the mean is very important in statistical analysis. In order to distinguish it from a standard deviation of the original measurements, it is given a special name: the **standard error.** So, the standard deviation of a collection of sample means is called the **standard error of the mean** (often abbreviated to **s.e.m.**), the standard deviation of a collection of sample medians is called the **standard error of the median,** and so on.

Suppose that the sample of five crampon shells that the person brought you had a mean length of 58·33 mm. You know that the standard error is 1·829 mm, and hence this sample mean is less than 1 standard error from the mean value for the sample means of 59·740 mm. Because the sample means are normally distributed, you can conclude that about 67% of them lie within one standard error of the mean. Hence, it is reasonable to accept the null hypothesis that this particular sample does indeed come from the British population of crampons. If, by contrast, the sample's mean shell length had been 66·58 mm, you would probably have come to a different conclusion.

☐ Work through the stages of reasoning for yourself.

■ 66·58 mm is more than 6·00 mm from the population mean. Figure 11 shows that none of the sample mean lengths are more than 6·00 mm from the mean of the sample means of 59·740: the probability of obtaining a sample with a mean length more than 6·00 mm from the mean value for the British population is very small. Therefore, you might think it reasonable to reject the null hypothesis that the sample comes from a population whose mean does not differ from that of the British population, and to accept the alternative hypothesis that it comes from a different population.

One further step in the argument is needed to make it applicable to a great deal of biological research. Suppose somebody brought you two samples of crampon shells rather than one, and asked whether they could have come from the same population. This is equivalent to setting up a null hypothesis that the samples come from populations that do not differ in their mean shell lengths. On the whole, you would expect that samples taken at random from the same population would tend to have mean shell lengths close to each other rather than far apart. If, for example, you were to look at any two of the 50 sample means in Table 4, and were to subtract one from the other, you would expect the answer to be close to zero. Table 5 shows the sort of result you would get if you were to take each of the 50 mean values in Table 4 in turn and subtract it from another mean in the Table chosen at random. Figure 12 presents such results as a histogram. Notice from Figure 12 that most of the differences are close to zero; that larger differences are progressively rarer; and that positive differences are as common as negative differences (because it is quite arbitrary which shell length you subtract from which). It turns out that these values are normally distributed, with a mean value of zero. Once again, it is possible to calculate the standard deviation of the differences in the means, in order to give an idea of how widely scattered they are about the mean; and once again, this kind of standard deviation is called a standard

Table 5 Differences between pairs of sample means taken from Table 4.

differences between pairs of means/mm				
−2·55	2·31	1·53	1·57	−0·79
3·32	−0·60	−1·50	0·38	5·12
−0·24	0·04	−3·40	−2·23	−3·08
2·27	3·24	5·19	0·47	−0·21
−2·21	−3·85	−7·02	0·34	0·41
1·86	−0·09	4·58	1·11	0·80
−0·76	−1·34	2·06	0·99	−1·00
−3·24	3·99	−0·19	1·08	0·69
2·05	−6·85	−0·94	−1·30	−1·24
2·99	6·37	−2·77	−2·40	0·66

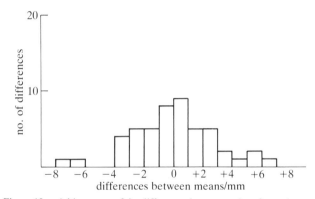

Figure 12. A histogram of the differences between pairs of sample means.

error—in this instance the **standard error of the difference in means.**

Just as with the original measurements of shell lengths and with the sample means, the knowledge that the differences in sample means are normally distributed makes it possible for us to calculate the probability of getting differences which are more than so many standard errors from the mean value. A large difference between the two sample means will be unlikely if the samples come from two populations with the same mean, whereas a small difference will be much more likely. It turns out that the standard error of the differences between sample means shown in Figure 12 is 2·772 mm. So, if samples are taken repeatedly from two populations of shells with the same mean length, then about 67% of the differences in sample means will be less than 2·772 mm, and about 95% of the differences will be less than twice 2·772 = 5·544 mm. Hence, if two samples of crampon shells were to differ in mean length by, say, 1·3 mm, you would accept the null hypothesis that they came from populations with the same mean shell length. On the other hand, if they were to differ in mean length by, say, 8·2 mm, you would have very strong grounds for rejecting the null hypothesis and for accepting the alternative hypothesis that they came from populations with different mean shell lengths.

In the preceding paragraphs we have considered three processes:
(i) deciding whether a single shell could have come from a known population;
(ii) deciding whether a sample of shells could have come from a known population;
(iii) deciding whether two samples could have come from the same population.
It is helpful to introduce now some additional ideas that apply to all three situations. In each, the procedure is as follows:

1   Set up a null hypothesis and an alternative hypothesis.

2   Look at the measurements obtained.

3   Find out the probability of getting results at least as extreme as these if the null hypothesis were true.

4   Reject the null hypothesis if this probability is too small, and accept the alternative hypothesis.

How small the probability has to be for you to reject the null hypothesis is a matter of personal judgement. It is usual in biology, however, to reject a null hypothesis only if the probability of obtaining your particular sets of measurements is less than 1 in 20. This probability is often written as a decimal, namely 0·05, or as a percentage, namely 5%. If you choose as your criterion for rejecting the null hypothesis a probability of 5%, you are said to be operating at a 5% **significance level**. Sometimes, you may find that the probability of obtaining the measurements that you have collected if the null hypothesis is true is a lot smaller than 1 in 20. It may be less than 1 in 100 or even less than 1 in 1 000. If so, you can then reject the null hypothesis at the 1% or the 0·1% levels respectively. There are several conventional methods of presenting significance levels in research reports. Table 6 lists some of those most commonly used.

Table 6   Four conventions for denoting significance levels.

less than 1 in 20	less than 1 in 100	less than 1 in 1000
5% level	1% level	0·1% level
$p < 0.05$	$p < 0.01$	$p < 0.001$
$0.01 < p < 0.05$	$0.001 < p < 0.01$	$0.0001 < p < 0.001$
*	**	***

2.4.2   Estimation

In the example described above, a significance test would enable you to decide whether the two shell samples could have come from the same population. You could, however, have used the arguments in virtually identical fashion to answer a different question: not 'Is there a difference in the population means?' but 'Within what range does the difference in population means lie?' This amounts to **estimating** that difference. If you look at Figure 12, you can see that virtually all the differences in sample means lie between −7 mm and +7 mm. In fact, because the differences in means are normally distributed, with a standard error of 2·772 mm, we know that 95% of them lie within a distance of two standard errors of the mean of this normal distribution. We assumed that the difference between the means of the *populations* from which the samples come was zero, so the mean of the distribution of differences in *sample means* is zero, and therefore 95% of the differences between sample means will lie between −5·544 mm and +5·544 mm (5·544 = 2 × 2·772). So far so good, but in practice you have only one pair of sample means, not the 50 in Table 4, and you cannot assume that the population means are equal—that is one of the things you probably want to investigate. If your pair of *sample means* differs by, say, 1·2 mm, and if the standard error of the difference in sample means is still 2·772 mm, then it is very likely that the difference between the *population means* is more than two standard errors from the difference you found, 1·2 mm. That is, a plausible range of values for the difference in population means runs from 1·2 − (2 × 2·772) mm to 1·2 + (2·772) mm, *i.e.* from −4·344 mm to +6·744 mm. We can be 95% confident of this, since 95% of the measurements in a normal distribution lie within two standard deviations of their mean. We can therefore refer to −4·344 mm and +6·744 mm as 95% **confidence limits** for the difference in population means. The range between upper and lower confidence limits is known as a 95% **confidence interval**.

Confidence limits can be very useful in, for example, agricultural research—see Section 1.3.5(i). If a fertiliser brings an increase in *sample mean* yield of, say, 100 kg of crop per unit area cultivated, with 95% confidence limits for the increase of 93 kg and 107 kg, then we know with 95% confidence that the difference in *population mean* yields between fertilised and unfertilised crops will lie between 93 kg and 107 kg per unit area. This information can be used in assessing whether it is economically worthwhile to use the fertiliser.

In Chapter 4 you will find that nearly every statistical technique that is described, can be used both to test a null hypothesis and to provide confidence limits. Both features are very useful, and which of them is more applicable to your project will depend upon the kind of question you are trying to answer.

2.4.3   Test statistics and critical values

The method for carrying out significance tests described in Section 2.4.1 contains some important features that need to be explained further. Take a situation where the null hypothesis under test is that the means of the populations from which two samples come are the same. In carrying out the test, you are in effect asking 'How likely is it that I would have obtained a difference in sample means at least as big as this if the null hypothesis were true?' Putting this in more general terms, you use the measurements from the two samples to calculate a *single* number; in this instance the difference in sample means. This is what happens in all significance tests described in this Project Guide, although the number you calculate will not always be the difference in sample means. This single number that you calculate in a significance test is called the **test statistic**.

An important feature of a test statistic is that it is always possible to calculate the probability of obtaining a particular value (of at least as large or as small as a given value) if the null hypothesis is true. Consider the shell example from Section 2.4.1. Look at Figure 13 which shows the relative frequency with which you would expect to find differences between pairs of sample means if the null hypothesis (that the two samples of shells came from the same population) were true. The Figure is very like Figure 12, but the histogram has been converted into a smooth curve, with a normal distribution, a mean of zero and a standard error of 2·772 mm, the same as for Figure 12. If we were to take the difference in sample means as a test statistic, then in formal terms we know its **probability distribution**. If you had decided upon a 5% significance level for your test, you would have been able to work out from the probability distribution how large a difference in sample means would be needed for the null hypothesis to be rejected. From Section 2.4.1 we know this value to be about twice the standard error, which is about 5·544 mm. Values larger than this (see Figure 13) allow us to reject the null hypothesis.

What we have done, in general terms, is to choose a **critical value** for the test statistic which, if exceeded, will cause you to reject your null hypothesis. So, in Figure 13, the critical value is 5·544 mm and you would reject the null hypothesis if the difference in sample means, the test statistic, exceeds this.

The following features are common to all significance tests:

1   You calculate a test statistic from your measurements.

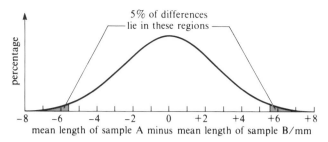

Figure 13.   The relative frequencies at which differences between pairs of sample means would be expected, under the null hypothesis that the means of the populations from which the samples were taken do not differ.

2   You know the probability distribution of this statistic, given that the null hypothesis is true.

3   You can discover from the probability distribution the critical value which your test statistic must exceed for the null hypothesis to be rejected.

The only probability distribution that you have come across so far is the normal distribution. It is important in biology, but by no means the only one. Others will be described in Chapter 4, which also tells you how to decide whether your test statistic really does follow a particular probability distribution.

Statisticians have taken a lot of the hard work out of significance testing, in particular by preparing Tables of critical values for given test statistics. Several such Tables are provided in Appendix III. This means that you can calculate a test statistic from your sample measurements and then simply consult the appropriate Table for the critical value under your null hypothesis for the significance level that you require. Tables frequently come in two versions, one for **'one-tailed'** or **'one-sided'** tests, and the other for **'two-tailed'** or **'two-sided'** tests. We recommend that you use the 'two-tailed' version. Only 'two-tailed' Tables are included in Appendix III.

Summary of Chapter 2

1   Statistical analysis involves making inferences from finite and often small samples about the populations from which the samples were drawn.

2   Different levels of measurement are possible: (i) interval level measurements, such as weight, length, time etc.; (ii) ordinal level measurements, where you can do no more than rank measurements with respect to one another; (iii) categorical level measurements, where you can do no more than classify your measurements into discrete, but non-rankable, categories.

3   Measurements may be either matched or unmatched. Where you have a choice, it is preferable to collect matched measurements.

4   It is extremely important to obtain a visual display of your measurements by using a lineplot, histogram, or scattergram or other means as appropriate, so that you can assimilate them.

5   The average value of the measurements from a sample can be calculated in the form of the sample mean or the sample median. The latter may be preferable when your measurements are strongly skewed.

6   The scatter of the measurements from your sample can be calculated in the form of the sample range or the sample standard deviation. The latter is more useful in almost all situations. The square of the sample standard deviation, called the sample variance, figures prominently in several of the techniques described in Chapter 4.

7   If several samples are taken from the same population, their sample means will vary one from another. The mean of these means will be close to the population mean. The standard deviation of this new mean is called the standard error of the mean. The standard deviations of other sample statistics (such as medians, or differences in sample means) are also called standard errors.

8   Hypothesis testing proceeds by formulating a null hypothesis and an alternative hypothesis. You calculate the probability of obtaining results that differ by at least as much as yours if the null hypothesis is true. If this probability is too small, conventionally less than 5%, you reject the null hypothesis and accept the alternative hypothesis. Such a test is called a **significance test.** It generates a **test statistic** whose value can be compared with tabulated critical values. If the test statistic exceeds the critical value for a given significance level, the null hypothesis can be rejected in favour of the alternative hypothesis at that level of significance.

9   Critical values can be used to produce estimates of the magnitude of differences between features of populations (such as means or medians) rather than simply deciding whether or not a difference exists.

Objectives for Chapter 2

You should now be able to:

★   Explain the difference between a statistical sample and a statistical population.

★   Explain the difference between interval, ordinal and categorical levels of measurements.

★   Explain the difference between symmetrical and skewed distributions.

★   Formulate null and alternative hypotheses.

★   Explain the difference between matched and unmatched measurements.

★   Display biological measurements in the form of histograms, lineplots or scattergrams, as appropriate.

★   Given appropriate sample measurements, calculate a sample mean, sample median, sample range, sample standard deviation and sample variance.

★   Explain what is meant by the terms standard error, standard error of the mean, and standard error of the difference in sample means.

★   List the main steps to be taken when carrying out a significance test.

★   Explain what is meant by the terms sample statistic, test statistic, critical value, confidence interval, and significance level.

★   Explain how a knowledge of the mean and standard deviation of a normal distribution can be used to generate probability values about test statistics that are normally distributed.

Chapter 3   Fieldwork techniques

For many ecological investigations, you will need to collect data about the *abundance* of organisms or their *pattern* of distribution. Clearly, you must be able to *identify* at least some of the species (or other taxa, see below) involved and, in the case of small active animals, this means that you will first have to *capture* them. For other projects, you will need to determine something about the organism's *cover, density frequency* or *performance*, (usually measured by size, shape, height, biomass or yield). Almost always you will have to measure the environmental factors that may have influenced the phenomenon under investigation. Chapter 3 is concerned with all these problems.

Correct **identification** is of fundamental importance to every project, so this is discussed first in Section 3.1. Section 3.2 considers the techniques relevant to the investigation of non-mobile plants and animals. Not surprisingly, it is necessary to adopt different approaches with mobile animals and free-floating plants; these are dealt with in Section 3.3. Methods of capturing these organisms are considered in Section 3.4 whilst Section 3.5 discusses the measurement of environmental factors. Section 3.6 gives advice on the devising of experiments to test hypotheses.

Remember that, in choosing your fieldwork technique, you should consider very carefully the way in which you are going to present and analyse your data and so design the data collection programme as to facilitate rather than complicate those stages of the project. You should be aware of the statistical tests you can use to analyse the different types of data—consult the Decision Chart on the inside back cover. Measurements of population size, density, frequency and percentage cover, for instance, are usually at the interval level but other kinds of data may be at the ordinal level (e.g. when using a frequency scale) or at the categorical level (see Section 2.2.1). Most statistical tests are available for interval level measurements. The choice of test will also influence the number of samples required (see Section 1.3.3).

Conservation of the site is an important consideration both when planning and carrying out fieldwork. When collecting your data in the field you should always be aware of the impact you can have on a site and you should devise methods to reduce any possible damage to an absolute minimum. The main rule is that you should aim to leave the site as you found it. Specimens should not be removed, even for later identification, unless it is obvious that the species is neither generally nor locally rare. Most sites are susceptible to trampling, some particularly so, and you should not visit or move about within them unnecessarily. Special problems arise if you have to make repeated visits to the same site and

these must be taken into account when planning. It will probably be best to define paths and exclude these from your sampling. This applies just as much to apparently resilient habitats (rocky sea shores, for example) as to obviously fragile ones.

When selecting the site(s) for your project, remember to obtain permission from the owner, not only for access but also for any particular activities (for example digging soil profiles) that you have in mind. Special restrictions apply in most Nature Reserves and, unless there is some overwhelming reason to the contrary, we suggest you avoid both them and Sites of Special Scientific Interest.

Remember to consider safety, both of yourself and other people. Observe sensible precautions; what is sensible for one person may not be sensible for another and a site that is perfectly safe under some circumstances may be hazardous under others. Great care should be taken when collecting samples from water particularly if you are working on your own, or from a boat. Acquaint yourself thoroughly with the study site, establish which access points are safe and make sure of your escape routes before you commence work. Do not attempt to work in, on or near rivers in spate and rocky shores in rough seas. Whenever you are working in a coastal habitat, *remember the tide*. Consider carefully its effect both on the timing of your work, and your safety. For further information we recommend the Institute of Biology's booklet 'Safety in Biological Fieldwork' (Nichols, 1983).

3.1   Identification

The value of your field data will depend on your ability to identify the plants and animals accurately. No matter how clear your presentation or how thorough your analyses may be, your whole project will be undermined by incorrect or inconsistent identification. We have already advised (Chapter 1) that you should concentrate on a few selected species; even then, correct identification and subsequent recognition may require considerable skill and experience, and it can be very time-consuming. Large groups present real problems—for example there are at least 20 000 species of insects in Britain! It is a good idea to use a pilot study to sort out identification problems. Ensure that you *can* recognise your selected organisms before you start to collect data about them. Should you, despite your precautions, encounter species that you do not recognise during the fieldwork it is best not to interrupt the data collection but to record them as 'species A', 'species B' etc. and substitute the real names later.

Note that it is not always necessary to identify everything

down to species level. In the first example of Section 1.1, there was no requirement to identify the species of moss, and similarly in hypothesis B3 (Table 1) the species of *Gammarus* is not mentioned. It is important, however, that you do not pretend to have identified plants or animals more accurately than is in fact the case. Most of the moss on the lawn may well be *Rhytidiadelphus squarrosus* but you should not use that name for the plants in your project unless you have identified each individual sampled. Similarly, throughout much of Britain *Gammarus pulex* is the common freshwater shrimp but you are only justified in using the specific name if you are certain that no *G. lacustris* or *G. duebeni* were included in the samples.

To identify an organism new to you will need to use an appropriate **key**. This will ask you to make a series of decisions based on morphological characteristics (characters) which, by a process of elimination, lead you to the correct identification. Unfortunately, keys vary greatly in their usefulness: 'popular' versions usually include only a small proportion of the species whilst some specialist works are comprehensible only to other specialists or cannot be used in the field. Some keys depend on seasonal characters (many botanical keys rely on the plant being in flower or in leaf) and may not work at other times. See Appendix I for some sources of keys and other aids to identification. To examine small organisms, and small features on larger ones, a hand lens is essential, whilst a binocular microscope makes the task considerably easier.

If, having run a specimen down in the appropriate key, you are still unsure about its identity, it is sometimes possible to consult reference collections held by local museums and Universities. The staff may also be able to put you in touch with a specialist willing to check your identification.

3.2 Abundance and distribution of non-mobile organisms

The techniques described in this Section are most commonly used in studies of plants, but they can often be applied or adapted to studies of relatively immobile and easily visible animals. Many seashore invertebrates (e.g., barnacles and limpets) come into this category and colonial species (e.g., sea mats and sponges) can only be studied by these means.

It is usually easier to collect data about **relative abundance** (either of different species in the same location or the same species in different locations) rather than absolute numbers. Measurements of relative abundance can be made in several ways. Sometimes you can count the number of individuals per unit area (i.e., measure the **density**). Alternatively, you can record how many sample areas include individuals of your selected species (i.e. measure **frequency**—how often each species is found). The third

common method is to assess the area of ground shaded by the selected species (the **cover**): the data are usually expressed as a proportion of the total ground area available (i.e. as **percentage cover**).

It is sometimes appropriate to measure or estimate, directly or indirectly, the total amount of plant material present: the weight of the living material or **biomass**. On other occasions, the **yield** (which can be regarded as the harvestable portion of the plant) may be a more suitable measure. For some comparative studies, the relative **size** may be adequate. For example, in a woodland project you could assess a stand of conifers by weighing them—but this would present horrendous practical problems. It would be easier (but still difficult) to deal with the yield, the timber removed for sale, if you happened to be on site at the right time. But measurements of trunk girth (which are related to biomass) provide excellent comparative data at a fraction of the cost.

Patterns of distribution can be investigated by comparing measurements of density, frequency, ground cover, biomass or yield in different parts of the study area. There are also techniques for assessing the degree of association between different species.

3.2.1   Subjective methods

As a start, you could simply make a 'species' list of the organisms present at your site, but more information can be given if you also record your *estimate* of their **relative abundance,** using one of the several subjective scales available. In the 'ACFOR' scale each 'species' present is assigned to one of the following categories

A = Abundant	F = Frequent
C = Common	O = Occasional
	R = Rare

When comparing two or more sites, a species may be present at one and not at the other. Under these circumstances, an additional category N = None Present is required.

Additional information about the growth form of each 'species' (e.g. shrub or field layer, single or in clumps) can be included to provide a very brief summary of the community.

PROBLEMS AND LIMITATIONS

● This technique is useful for initial studies only.

● It is highly subjective—two independent observers may disagree on the description of the same area.

● The relative abundance of conspicuous organisms (e.g. plants in flower) will tend to be overestimated and that of inconspicuous ones underestimated.

● Data based on subjective estimates should not be analysed statistically.

Table 7. Abundance scales for use in rocky shore survey work originally devised by Crisp & Southward (1958). This version follows that modified by Dr Keith Hiscock of the Field Studies Council's Oil Pollution Research Unit. It uses quadrats of three sizes: 1 m^2, 0.1 m^2 and 0.01 m^2.

1. Algae
E. More than 90% cover
S. 60–89% cover
A. 30–59% cover
C. 5–29% cover
F. Less than 5% cover but zone still apparent
O. Scattered plants, zone indistinct
R. Only one or two plants present

2. Lichens and *Lithothamnion*
E. More than 80% cover
S. 50–79% cover
A. 20–49% cover
C. 1–19% cover
F. Large scattered patches
O. Widely scattered patches, all small
R. Only one or two small patches present

3. Small barnacles and small winkles
E. 500 or more 0.01 m^{-2}
S. 300–499 0.01 m^{-2}
A. 100–299 0.01 m^{-2}
C. 10–99 0.01 m^{-2}
F. 1–9 0.01 m^{-2}
O. 1–99 m^{-2}
R. Less than 1 m^{-2}

4. Limpets and large winkles
E. 20 or more 0.1 m^{-2}
S. 10–19 0.1 m^{-2}
A. 5–9 0.1 m^{-2}
C. 1–4 0.1 m^{-2}
F. 5–9 m^{-2}
O. 1–4 m^{-2}
R. Less than 1 m^{-2}

5. Large barnacles *Balanus perforatus*
E. 300 or more 0.01 m^{-2}
S. 100–299 0.01 m^{-2}
A. 10–99 0.01 m^{-2}
C. 1–9 0.01 m^{-2}
F. 1–9 0.1 m^{-2}
O. 1–9 m^{-2}
R. Less than 1 m^{-2}

6. Dogwhelks, Topshells and Anemones
E. 10 or more 0.1 m^{-2}
S. 5–9 0.1 m^{-2}
A. 1–4 0.1 m^{-2}
C. 5–9 m^{-2}, locally sometimes more
F. 1–4 m^{-2}, locally sometimes more
O. Less than 1 m^{-2}, locally sometimes more
R. Always less than 1 m^{-2}

7. Mussels and Piddocks (score holes)
E. More than 80% cover
S. 50–79% cover
A. 20–49% cover
C. 5–19% cover
F. Small patches, covering less than 5% of the rock surface
O. 1–9 individuals m^{-2}: No patches
R. Less than 1 individual m^{-2}

8. Tube worms such as *Pomatoceros*
A. 50 or more tubes 0.01 m^{-2}
C. 1–49 tubes 0.01 m^{-2}
F. 1–9 tubes 0.1 m^{-2}
O. 1–9 tubes m^{-2}
R. Less than 1 tube m^{-2}

E = Extremely abundant
S = Super abundant
A = Abundant
C = common
F = frequent
O = occasional
R = rare
N = absent

The ACFOR scale can be made less subjective by defining the categories. 'Abundant' might be defined as 'ground cover of 75% or more' and so on. However, what is 'abundant' for one species may be 'frequent' for another and it may be helpful to construct different sets of criteria for different types of organism. It was developments of this process that lead to the formulation of a series of **Abundance Scales** for the common seashore animals and plants, a recent version of which is reproduced in Table 7. Ordinal level data (Section 2.2.1) of this form *can* be analysed by some statistical techniques—consult the Decision Chart on the inside back cover.

3.2.2 Quantitative Methods: quadrat sampling techniques

The theory of sampling to obtain information about

populations was discussed in Section 2.1. In practice, two sampling techniques form the basis for several different ways of collecting data. The first uses a frame to mark out the sample *area* on the ground. **Frame quadrats** (Figure 14), as their name implies, are usually four-sided and often square, but may be of any convenient shape. Alternatively sample *points* can be recorded using a **point quadrat**. A common version of the apparatus (a point frame) required for this approach is illustrated in Figure 15. The 'point' being sampled is where the tip of the pointer touches the vegetation.

Both types of quadrat frame can be made quite easily. Large frame quadrats are conveniently made from four strips of wood bolted together at the corners. This enables you to dismantle or fold the frame for easy carrying.

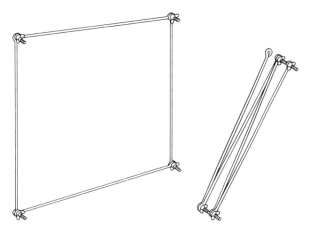

Figure 14. A convenient, collapsible, design of frame quadrat.

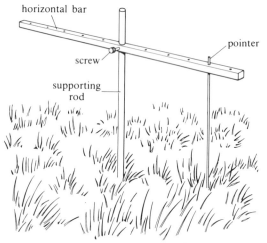

Figure 15. A point quadrat frame.

Smaller frame quadrats can best be made from thick-gauge wire or brazing rod. The point frames illustrated in Figure 15 and on the front cover are made of metal, but you could easily adapt the design to construct your own out of wood. A sharpened central rod is usually the best way to support the frame but for work on hard surfaces you require some sort of tripod. Long knitting needles, or old bicycle spokes can be used as pointers. Theoretically, a point has no area, so, in practice, the tip of the pin should be as sharp as possible to improve the accuracy of the data.

Some examples of the use of quadrat sampling methods are

— measurement of relative abundance within a defined area;
— comparisons of abundance within the same defined area at different times;

— comparison of abundance between two different defined areas;
— changes in distribution or abundance along a line of transition from one habitat to another (transect studies);
— association studies—to determine whether one species is positively (or negatively) associated with another.

Some of the ways in which a frame quadrat can be used are described in Section 3.2.5 and those for a point quadrat in 3.2.6.

3.2.3   Choosing the Sample Areas

There are two decisions to be taken: how many samples you should take and how they should be distributed. The problem of deciding on the number of samples was discussed in Section 1.3; this Section is concerned with their distribution.

The choice is whether to select sample sites in a **systematic** (=regular) manner or at **random**. The systematic approach may appear more logical since it ensures that all parts of the study area are evenly sampled. However, man-made and man-managed habitats can be assumed to have an imposed regularity to a greater or lesser degree. Trees and other crops are usually planted, managed and harvested in straight lines. It is recommended that a random sampling procedure be adopted in such cases to avoid the possibility of bias should a systematic sampling procedure happen to coincide with the regularity of the habitat. It is sometimes difficult to detect human influence but it can be assumed for almost all the land surface of Britain.

The essential ingredient for a **random distribution of sample areas** is that each area must have an equal chance of being chosen for each sample. You may have heard that ecologists select random positions by throwing quadrat frames over their shoulders. A quick consideration of the factors influencing this activity (such as the thrower's strength) should convince you that this practice can never result in a random distribution. It has been abandoned by all self-respecting ecologists.

The following example outlines the simplest situation to provide you with an idea of the general procedure. Let us imagine that your designated study area is conveniently flat and square (10 m × 10 m). Your actual location is unlikely to be perfectly square or horizontal and will doubtless present some minor problems. A length of string is laid out along one edge, marked off at 1 m intervals; these intervals are numbered 1 to 10 (for larger areas it is convenient to use pegs as markers). A second edge, at right angles to the first, is marked off in a similar manner. Right angles are easily established using a 3,4,5 triangle [You need three pegs and a piece of string with a loop at each end, marked out in sections of 3, 4, and 5 units long. With both loops over one peg, fix the 3-unit length as your base line and push in the second peg when the string is taut. If the rest of the string is also kept taut, the third peg, placed at the mark between the 4-unit and 5-unit sections, can only be positioned so as to produce a right-angle between the 3 and 4-unit sections.] The numbered marks (along each 10 m side) can be used to define the co-ordinates of any 1 m × 1 m square within the 10 m × 10 m area. Random selection of sample squares is now straightforward: a pair of numbers between 1 and 10 drawn at random will locate the position of the first quadrat. A second pair will locate the next, and so on.

Many calculators can generate a short sequence of (pseudo-) random numbers. Alternatively, pairs of numbers to provide the co-ordinates can be taken from a Table of **Random Numbers** such as Table III(1) in Appendix III. Select any number as the starting point and then work through the table in a regular manner. Do not be surprised if the same co-ordinates turn up twice—remember that every point within your area must have an equal chance of being selected each time.

(It is possible to use sampling sites at random in such a way that prevents the same point being selected twice, but the analysis of the data gained from this kind of sampling sometimes requires statistical methods beyond the scope of this book.)

Whatever method you devise, you must ensure that:

(1) If you are using a frame quadrat, the length of each side of your study area is an exact multiple of the length of the quadrat side, otherwise either some parts of your area will be excluded from your sampling or the sample areas will overlap. (Note that your choice of quadrat size depends on other factors as well—see Section 3.2.4.)

(2) Each sample area must have an equal chance of being sampled each time—and that includes the areas from which you have already collected data.

(3) You must avoid trampling the vegetation at future sampling points, particularly when assessing cover. Where possible, having selected the sampling points at random, actually collect the data by working across the study area in a regular manner. But beware of time-related changes if sampling of the whole area covers an extended period. Otherwise, any pattern which emerges may be due to temporal influences—not spatial differences within your sample area.

If it is impossible to mark out a square area as a study site, you can devise a system of **random walking**. A pair of random numbers is used to determine the number of paces forward and then at right angles (spinning a coin to decide whether to turn left or right) from starting point to sample point. It is best to start from the same point each time but, if this is impracticable, be sure that the system you devise really is randomised: the range of numbers from which you select must allow each point within the study area to have an equal chance of being sampled each time. This technique may produce an unacceptable level of trampling and should only be chosen if this will not affect the data.

There are instances where it is appropriate to select a **systematic sampling** procedure. The most common example is along a transect where data are collected at regular spacings along a line (see Section 3.2.7), but it may also be used where the intention is to produce a rough map to delimit a distribution pattern. The attributes of systematic and random sampling may be combined, e.g. by random sampling in a small area at each of the regular spacings along the transect. This is an example of **stratified random sampling.** It can be used to investigate distribution patterns or, in a site susceptible to damage by trampling, when you wish to reduce your impact to a few discrete areas.

3.2.4 Choosing the size and shape of your frame quadrat

Different sizes of frame quadrat are appropriate to different types of investigation and different sizes of organisms. A 0·01 m² square (100 mm × 100 mm) is used for assessing the abundance of the green alga *Pleurococcus* on tree bark and of barnacles on a rocky shore, whilst quadrat areas of several square metres are required in woodland for estimating the abundance of different tree species.

The choice of quadrat size must depend to some extent on the type of community being studied. A general rule of thumb is that if the individuals are larger than the quadrats you are using, you need larger quadrats! Most field-type vegetation can be sampled using a 0·25 m² square (0·5 m × 0·5 m). Large frames are difficult to handle on rough ground and amongst dense vegetation, although a 1 m² frame is sometimes more suitable for estimating percentage cover because it can be divided easily into 100 smaller squares of a useful size using lengths of string or fishing line.

Frame quadrats can be of any regular shape. Rectangular 'quadrats' have advantages in some circumstances; for example, they can be more efficient in identifying striated patterns of distribution. Circular and even hexagonal 'quadrats' have been used successfully in some studies. The detailed arguments about their relative efficiency need not concern us here but *whatever shape is used the area must be known*. This probably explains the popularity of square frames! When comparing two sites, or your own data with published work, it is advisable to use quadrats of the same size and shape.

3.2.5 Using the frame quadrat

For all recording methods, it is necessary to draw up a list of those species relevant to your particular study. Remember that there is no need to identify everything to species level, but that you must be consistent through the study, always calling the same organism by the same name.

(a)   To measure density

To measure the density of a 'species' within your selected area, count all the individuals present within your chosen quadrats and extrapolate to give the total number for the whole area. Alternatively, the density can be expressed as an average figure per square metre (m^{-2}). Refer to Section 1.3 for advice on how many quadrats you need to take. Note that in comparative studies it may not be necessary to measure density. Frequency measurements are often quicker and easier—see (c) below.

PROBLEMS AND LIMITATIONS OF THE FRAME QUADRAT

● This method can only be used when dealing with clearly-defined and separate individuals (e.g. seedlings, trees, limpets etc). Many plants do not grow as individuals. Flowering plants may spread by suckers, tillers, runners or rhizomes, with the result that many apparently separate shoots may all be of the same individual. Lichen patches grow together and coalesce, with the result that what appear to be single colonies actually may be composed of many.

● Around the margins, many larger individuals will only be partially included within the quadrat and it will be necessary to choose some arbitrary criterion for inclusion (e.g., main stem must be within the quadrat if that individual is to be counted).

● At high densities, it can be difficult to ensure that every individual within the quadrat has been counted. Using a smaller quadrat may solve this problem. Note that you do not have to sample all species within a community using the same size quadrat (see Table 7).

● The method can be very time-consuming unless densities are low.

(b)   To measure percentage cover

When densities are high, or the counting of individuals is impractical for other reasons, an indication of relative abundance can be obtained by recording the proportion of the ground covered by each species. A rough indication can be obtained using a frame quadrat divided into a 10×10 grid with string or fishing line. Carefully place the quadrat over the selected sample area (causing as little disturbance as possible). For each species on your list, first count the number of squares fully occupied; then, the number that are partly occupied and estimate how many full squares this represents. Sum the totals to give a value for the percentage

cover. Also count the number of squares (if any) in which there are no individuals (of the species on your list). Since each small square within a 10×10 grid represents 1% of the total area of the quadrat, summing all your values should give 100%. Another way of dealing with the partly-filled squares is to include all those with half or more than half of the area covered, and exclude all those with less.

PROBLEMS AND LIMITATIONS

● It is difficult to assess cover when the plants in your study area are of very different heights.

● Smaller species underneath a canopy of larger ones are often ignored.

● Large leafy plants are often overestimated compared with other methods.

● It can be time-consuming unless there is only a small number of species to be sampled.

(c)   To measure frequency of occurrence

The **frequency** of a species indicates the chance of finding it within a given sample area; thus, if it has a frequency of 10% you would expect to find it in one out of every 10 quadrats you sampled. Frequency measurements are particularly useful when you cannot use density but want to compare the abundance of one species (or a small number of selected species) in different locations.

First, record whether each of the species on your list is 'present' or 'absent' in a number of sample quadrats. For each of those species, keep a cumulative score of the number of quadrats containing at least one representative (= present) and of those which do not (= absent). The 'present' score for each species can be used as an index of frequency; if you express the score as a percentage of the total number of quadrats the result will be a **percentage frequency**. Quadrats divided into 10×10 grids (as in (b) above) can provide 100 recordings, and will allow you to record **local frequency** (as a percentage) for each sample area. The fewer the subdivisions of the quadrat, the faster the recording time; but the fewer data there are from each sample area the less useful is the result.

There is a distinction between **root frequency** and **shoot frequency**. If you record a plant as present only when it is rooted in the sample area you are measuring root frequency (which is related to density). If you record the plant as present if any part of its foliage is within the area, you are recording shoot frequency (which is related to cover). Shoot frequency is generally the more useful measure.

The problem of underestimating the abundance of small plants (inherent with percentage cover measurements) is reduced if you use this method, provided that you inspect each sample area carefully for all the selected species.

PROBLEMS AND LIMITATIONS

● The frequency value can vary with quadrat size so you should quote the quadrat size when presenting your results.

● As when recording density, you must establish a criterion for including or excluding those individuals that overlap the edge of the sample area (i.e. decide whether to measure shoot or root frequency).

● There are problems inherent in the interpretation of frequency data for species that are obviously clumped.

3.2.6 Using the point quadrat

One limitation of the frame quadrat, particularly for an assessment of percentage cover, is that you must use your judgement to decide whether more or less than half of each square is covered by the selected species. This judgement becomes easier as you decrease the size of the sample area because each plant is more likely either to cover fully, or to be entirely absent from, a very small square. Decreasing the size of the square to an absolute minimum reduces it, in effect, to a single point. This is the rationale for using a point quadrat: instead of making estimates in a sample *area* you record presence or absence at a number of *points*. Sample sites may be selected randomly or systematically, as for the frame quadrat.

As with other sampling techniques, it is necessary to establish a list of those species relevant to your particular study. As before, there is no need to identify everything to species level, but that you must be consistent through the study, always calling the same organism by the same name. It is also necessary to decide how many sample areas are required and how they should be distributed (see Sections 1.3 and 3.2.3).

In use, the point frame is supported above the vegetation on its central rod (Figure 15: p. 26) or on a tripod for work on hard ground. The bar provides ten point-locations per sample and holds the pointer steady in a vertical position. Pass the pointer in turn through each of the ten holes in the horizontal bar and record the species touched by the tip of the pointer as it is lowered to the ground. The method of recording depends upon which type of data you require:—

(a) **Relative numbers** of individuals (of one or more 'species') may be estimated although it is not possible to measure density itself. This is because the sample points have no area (in theory) and, therefore, you cannot relate numbers to area. As with density measurements, this approach presupposes that you can recognise individuals.

(b) The **total cover** of each 'species' can be recorded, which may be used as an index related to biomass. It is not a direct estimate of biomass (which is a weight) but when comparing similar types of vegetation, values for total cover can be assumed to vary with values for biomass.

(c) **Proportional cover**—the proportion of the ground shaded by the aerial parts of the organism—can be recorded in two ways: either simply record those plants which form the canopy and shade the others, or record the plants growing in the shade of others as well. In the latter case, the percentage cover of all the species added together may well exceed 100% because several will overlap and shade the same patch of ground.

(d) Data on **frequency**—the chance of finding a species within a given area—can be collected quite rapidly using a point frame, by adapting the 'presence' or 'absence' recording system described for the frame quadrat.

The differences in the methods of recording are subtle and may seem rather trivial. It is all too easy to vary your method as you progress through the sample stations,

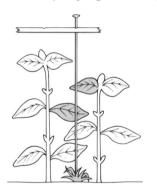

(a) **relative numbers** of each 'species': score the first hit on each individual plant.

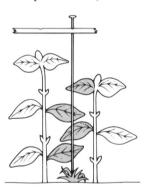

(b) **total cover**: score all hits.

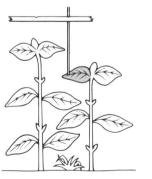

(c) **top canopy cover**: score first hit only.

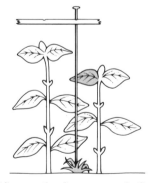

(d) **proportional cover**: score the first hit on each 'species'.

Figure 16. Different ways in which data may be collected using a point frame. Shaded portions of the plants indicate the scores made by the tip of the pointer.

ending up with a useless set of hybrid data. Decide at the outset which is the most suitable form of measurement; test it in a pilot study, and then be consistent in your method of recording.

(a) To sample for relative numbers

At each point location, record each touch of the point on *each new individual* as the pointer is lowered to the ground *'First hit on each new individual'* scoring—(Figure 16a); keep a cumulative score for each species as you work through an appropriate number of stations.

(b) To sample for total cover

At each point location record every touch of the point on the aerial parts of each individual *'All Hits'* scoring (Figure 16b).

(c) To sample for proportional cover (usually converted to percentage cover)

To measure the top canopy cover, simply record the first individual touched by the tip of the pointer at each point location—*'First Hit'* scoring (Figure 16c).

To obtain the percentage cover for each of your selected species (including those growing in the shade of others) you should record the *First hit on each new species* at each point location (Figure 16d). Provided sufficient points are taken, this method can avoid the problem of underestimating the cover of smaller plants.

Whichever approach you adopt, keep a cumulative record of the number of 'hits' and express the total number as a percentage of *all the point-locations* sampled, including those at which all the species on your list are absent.

(d) To sample for frequency of occurrence

At each sampling station, record whether each species is

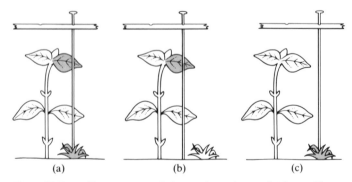

Figure 17. Recording presence and absence data using a point frame. The shaded areas indicate the hits (by the tip of the pointer) to be recorded. (a) both species (b) only the tall species (c) only the short species.

present (one or more hits at *any* of the ten point locations) or absent (no hits). Figure 17 shows three different situations and how they should be recorded. For each of the selected species, keep a cumulative score of the *number of sample stations* at which it is present. Express the frequency for each species as a percentage of the total number of sample stations. You must record at a large number of sample stations (e.g. up to 100 with ten point-locations at each) to obtain an estimate with acceptable confidence limits. This may appear time-consuming, but the procedure can become fairly rapid with practice and you do not have to inspect an area thoroughly in order to check for the possible presence of rarities, as is the case with a frame quadrat.

Note that a point frame can be used for canopy-cover estimates if you lie underneath it and look upwards through the holes.

PROBLEMS AND LIMITATIONS OF THE POINT QUADRAT

- Point frames are difficult to use when the vegetation is higher than the height of the horizontal bar, and where the vegetation is layered with some of it above and some below the bar.

- Methods which depend on the distinguishing of individual plants are no easier with points than with frames.

- Plants with ascending leaves are under-estimated (with respect to frequency) relative to those with spreading leaves. Plants with long narrow leaves are overestimated relative to those with circular ones.

- You must avoid trampling the vegetation at future sampling points, particularly when assessing cover. Where possible, having selected the sampling points at random, actually collect the data in a regular manner across the study area.

- You must beware of time-related factors and influences when sampling over an extended period.

3.2.7 Other types of investigation involving quadrat sampling

(a) Transects

To investigate the transition from one community to another, particularly when they are arranged in a linear sequence (e.g. up a seashore or across a woodland margin) a transect technique may be appropriate. If the data are collected along a single line this is called a **line transect**. You simply list all the individuals in order along the line. A single line transect is unlikely to be representative of the site and it is necessary to take a series of lines. It is often better to examine sample areas within a broader strip, to produce a **belt transect.** The selection of sample sites along a transect is one case where a systematic method of sampling is usually adopted. If it is necessary to incorporate a random element, e.g. to eliminate human influence (see Section 3.2.3), a stratified random approach may be adopted. The sample areas are selected in a systematic manner along the transect, but the data are collected at random within those areas.

Depending on the distances involved you may carry out a **continuous transect,** in which you sample the whole line or belt, or an **interrupted transect,** in which samples are taken at (usually regular) positions, leaving gaps between the stations.

The same considerations, discussed in Section 3.2.4 with regard to the size of quadrats, apply to the width of a belt transect and thus the two should be compatible. When studying terrestrial vegetation, there is usually no need for a very wide belt. The minimum width of the belt will be the width of the frame quadrat, or the length of the bar on your point frame. Measurements of local frequency, using a frame quadrat subdivided into smaller squares, can be a useful technique when adopting this type of systematic sampling. However, in more dispersed and patchy communities a wider belt is required; on rocky shores, 5 m or even wider belts are often used. For some analyses, you will need to take several samples at each station along the transect.

When using an interrupted transect, you can select the sample points at regularly spaced *horizontal* or *vertical* intervals. The latter is obviously more appropriate when seeking to study a distribution pattern which is itself dependent on some physical factor related to height, for example changes in vegetation up a mountain, up a tree trunk or up a sea shore.

Figure 18 illustrates two methods of surveying on a slope where it is necessary to record the vertical and/or horizontal distances between sample areas. **Transect poles** (Figure 18a) are a convenient method when the vertical interval is small. In the illustration, data are to be collected at set (2 m) horizontal intervals but there is no reason why the technique should not be adapted to the vertical interval, i.e. keep *y* constant and record the different lengths of *x*.

For longer horizontal distances, a water-filled tube or a piece of taut string (with a spirit level slung beneath it) may be used in place of the 2 m pole. Dropping perpendiculars at regular intervals from the horizontal pole and noting the distances to the ground enables you to draw the **profile** (Figure 18b).

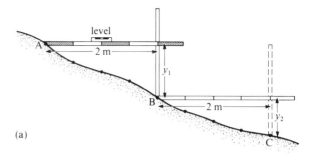

(a)

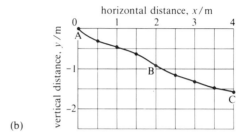

(b)

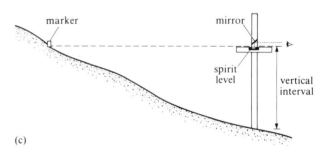

(c)

Figure 18.   Surveying on a slope where it is necessary to record the vertical and/or horizontal distances between sample areas.
(a) **transect poles** are a convenient method when the vertical interval is small. Data are collected at set horizontal or vertical intervals.
(b) Dropping perpendiculars at regular intervals from the horizontal pole and noting the distances to the ground, enables you to draw the profile. Note that you do not have to have both axes drawn to the same scale (as in this case).
(c) The **cross staff** is more practical to use, especially when working on your own, when using a fixed vertical interval.

The **cross staff** (Figure 18c) is more practical when using a fixed vertical interval (provided it is not too small!), for larger distances and when working alone. On the shore, it is conventional to use a cross staff of a height roughly equal to 10% of the tidal range. In other habitats, decide on how many samples you wish to take, determine the total vertical height and proceed accordingly. It is possible to survey up or down from your baseline using a cross staff, but it is certainly quicker to work upwards.

Table 8 A contingency table of presence and absence data for association studies.

		Species B	
		present	absent
Species A	present	(a)	(b)
	absent	(c)	(d)

Table 9 A contingency table using nearest neighbour data for association studies.

		base individual	
		A	B
nearest neighbour	A	(a)	(b)
	B	(c)	(d)

(b) Association studies

Presence or absence data obtained from quadrat sampling can be used to determine whether two species are associated, either positively or negatively. The principle was discussed in Section 2.2.1 (p. 9). The data obtained allow you to group your quadrats (or sample squares) into four categories. If you were studying two species, A and B, the four categories would be:—

(a) Both A and B present

(b) A present and B absent

(c) A absent and B present

(d) Both A and B absent.

The number of quadrats in each category can be presented as a **Contingency Table** (Table 8). The resulting data can be subjected to a χ^2 test (Section 4.8).

PROBLEMS AND LIMITATIONS

● Association studies from quadrat analysis depend very much on the size of quadrat used. Take the example in Figure 19; if the quadrats and the plants are approximately equal in size (quadrat size 1) most quadrats will contain only species A or B or C. The size 2 quadrats will mostly show the expected pattern of species A and B together and C alone. The large, size 3, quadrat is likely to include all three species most of the time. And, just to add to the problems, the analysis of association is also affected by quadrat spacing.

We can get round this problem by adopting a **plotless sampling** method, as follows. A number of sample individuals of species A (later repeated for species B) are selected. These are termed **base individuals**. For each base individual, the nearest neighbour (whether species A or B) is found by measuring the distance between and is recorded. A **contingency table,** like Table 9, can then be drawn up. This time (a) represents the number of times that a plant of species A is the nearest neighbour to another plant of species A etc. These data can be subjected to a χ^2 test. Section 4.8 describes the appropriate statistical handling of these kinds of data.

3.2.8 Other types of measurements: yield and performance

For some projects, a measure of **performance** is more useful than one relating to abundance. Direct measurements of **yield** (the dry weight of material harvested from each species grown in an area of known size) are perfectly possible but they are, of course, destructive and are not usually an acceptable method of collecting field data. However, it may be the most appropriate method of assessing the result of field experiments designed to test the effect of a fertiliser, weed killer, or insecticide on the performance of selected plants. The yield is determined by clipping (or otherwise harvesting) the individuals present in a number of frame quadrats, separating them into the (selected) species, drying and weighing them. This dry weight can then be used to estimate the yield per square metre.

For a given plant species, there is a relationship between total cover (see Section 3.2.6.b) and biomass. An indirect estimate of *relative* biomass may thus be obtained from values of total cover. This can only be used for the same species in different locations or at different times in the same location. As the relationship depends on growth form, it cannot be used to compare different types of plant.

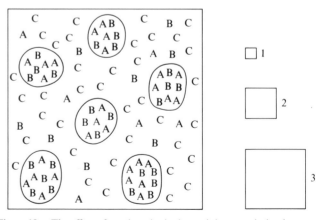

Figure 19. The effect of quadrat size in determining association between three species, A, B and C. For an explanation, see the text above left.

Other indicators of plant performance include measures related to the photosynthetic ability of individuals (e.g. the ratio of leaf length to leaf width) and reproductive capability (e.g. the number (or weight) of the flowers or seeds produced). Mention has already been made of tree girth and total cover measurements as indications of size. Growth can be recorded by measuring the same individual at different times. Likewise the rate of destruction, especially of leaves, can be measured directly. Examining the same oak leaves morning and evening in May, when leaves are growing and caterpillars are feeding, can give measurable changes.

Length and breadth of shelled invertebrates are easily measured. So is weight, which may be expected to vary with shell thickness. Soft-bodied invertebrates which have no fixed shape are best weighed, although it may be more appropriate to measure their volume (by the water displaced when they are submerged). The problem with measuring body weight, especially when dealing with certain aquatic organisms, like sea anemones, is that their weight in air is highly dependent upon the amount of water retained in or around their body. For accurate measurement, dry weight is taken (dried to constant weight in a desiccator) but this is only possible with dead material. The usual compromise is to shake or blot off as much superficial water as possible before weighing. For comparative studies it is sufficient to treat all specimens in exactly the same manner before and during the weighing procedure, when the errors will be common to all measurements.

You must select a valid indicator, and a convenient means of measuring it, appropriate to your particular investigation.

3.3 Abundance and distribution of mobile organisms

Most of the techniques described in Sections 3.3 and 3.4 relate to the study of invertebrate animals and the methods of capturing them. Details of the methods for trapping vertebrates are not given and *we would advise novices not to embark on projects which involve the capture of birds or mammals.* Such work often requires considerable skill, expensive sophisticated equipment and (in many cases) a special licence.

For successful fieldwork with mobile animals, you need to know something about the distribution of the species within the habitat, and of their behaviour patterns. For example, peppered moths, *Biston betularia,* rest on tree trunks during the day and fly actively by night. It is very difficult to count them by day, but males are easily attracted to a moth trap at night. If the sex ratio is known,

the numbers so captured can be taken as an index of the whole population. Alternatively, counts of moth eggs can give an estimate of density provided the behaviour of the egg-laying females is sufficiently understood.

If you know where your selected animals are to be found at certain times, and how they behave under certain circumstances, you can devise techniques to sample them efficiently and consistently. Very often, this kind of information will not be found in books and can be gained only by careful observation at your chosen site.

Some of the sampling techniques we describe involve killing a proportion of the population, and you must decide whether or not this is acceptable. If you wish to return your captured individuals to their original habitat you must plan accordingly and use a technique that will not harm them.

3.3.1 Sampling strategies for estimating numbers of mobile animals

Many of the principles discussed in Section 3.2 also apply to mobile animals. It is seldom possible to count all the individuals within a population and total numbers have to be estimated from appropriate samples. However, the difficulties in applying a sensible sampling strategy are increased considerably when dealing with mobile organisms. Distribution patterns can change rapidly, whilst emigration and immigration can drastically affect population size. Mobile animals are rarely distributed in a uniform manner and sampling methods involving quadrats can seldom be used. The actual sample size is often determined more by the number of individuals you can catch than by any theoretical consideration.

To compare the relative numbers of individuals in different sites you must standardise your sampling strategy and technique for all locations. This can be difficult if different sites present different problems—for instance, sampling from still and flowing water or collecting insects in windy and sheltered locations. It is often advisable to try several techniques in a pilot study to establish which is the most appropriate. One comparison of two alternative methods for trapping air-borne insects showed that water traps caught nearly three times as many insects as did sticky traps, but that sticky traps provided the more consistent samples—at least in that habitat (see Section 3.4.2). With hunting techniques that rely on your own skill and activity, the catch rate often increases as you become more familiar with the method. It is advisable to practise in a similar location before starting to collect data for your project, so that you eliminate 'teething troubles' and gain experience.

3.3.2 Direct estimates of total numbers

(a)   Number per microstand

Where the animals being studied are distributed at a

number of discrete and easily recognisable parts of an ecosystem (e.g. woodlice under stones or logs), it is sometimes possible to count the total number of individuals within a few representative microstands (stones or logs) and then extrapolate to produce an estimate of the total number in the whole community. You must, of course, be able to count (or estimate) the number of microstands at the site. Decisions about how many microstands to sample, and how they should be selected, depend on the same reasoning we applied to quadrats in Sections 3.2.3 and 3.2.4.

(b)   Number per unit area

Where distribution is more uniform, the total number of individuals in representative sample areas can be counted—for instance, the number of aphids per leaf. It is sometimes possible to use a quadrat method in these cases when a mobile animal becomes effectively immobile at certain times.

(c)   Number per unit volume

For small organisms distributed fairly uniformly in water, soil or leaf litter, counting the number of individuals obtained from a sample of known volume is sometimes possible.

3.3.3   Indirect estimates of total numbers

(a)   Mark–release–recapture

A much-quoted method of estimating the total population of a mobile animal within a clearly-defined site uses a **mark–release–recapture** procedure. A sample of the population is captured. Each individual is marked in a non-harmful way (e.g. a spot of paint applied to the thorax of an insect) and released to mix with the remainder of the population. The capture procedure is repeated later, when the proportion of marked individuals in the second sample can be used to estimate the number in the total population. The ratio of the number of individuals caught and marked in the first sample (S_1) to the total number N in the population is the same as the ratio of the number recaptured (R) to the total caught in the second sample (S_2) (Figure 20). Using these symbols:

$S_1 : N$ is the same as $R : S_2$

this can be re-written as

$$\frac{S_1}{N} = \frac{R}{S_2}$$

and re-arranged as

$$N = \frac{S_1 \times S_2}{R}$$

This is the Lincoln–Peterson Method and the estimate of the total number of individuals in the population so obtained is called the **Lincoln Index.** At least 10% of the marked and released sample (and preferably not less than 7

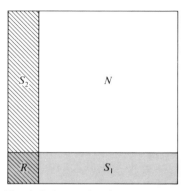

Figure 20. The Lincoln Index, mark–release–recapture technique for estimating population size. The areas in the figure are proportional to the numbers of individual animals involved. Thus the total area represents N, the population size. S_1 (shaded area) and S_2 (cross-hatched area) are the number caught in the first and second samples respectively. R (the overlap of S_1 and S_2) represents the number of individuals captured in sample 1, marked, released and recaptured in sample 2.
If R, S_1 and S_2 are known, N can be calculated.

individuals) should be in the second sample if a reasonable estimate is to be made. You should continue sampling until at least this level has been reached.

The 95% confidence limits of the estimation of N (within which the true value of N lies) are given by:—

$$N \pm \left(2N \sqrt{\frac{1}{R} - \frac{1}{S_2}} \right)$$

[see Section 2.4.2 for an explanation of confidence limits]

PROBLEMS AND LIMITATIONS

● The method is suitable only for species which live in discrete populations inhabiting a definable area, and whose individuals are not territorial but mingle at random.

● If the animals change their distribution patterns at different times of day (if, for example, they spend part of the day feeding on leaves and the rest at the base of the stem) they must be resampled under comparable conditions.

● The released individuals must be allowed sufficient time to mix randomly with the remainder of the population between sampling. For flying insects 3–4 hours may be sufficient in warm weather but for most other animals longer periods will be required. If the species is most active at night, or at high tide, you must allow a night or a period of high tide between sampling.

● The index assumes that the total population does not change between the two samples (no births or deaths;

no immigration and no emigration). The longer the time interval between capture and recapture the more suspect this assumption becomes.

● The capture technique, used to obtain the original sample, must not alter the habitat.

● The trapping and marking technique must not harm the animals, affect their behaviour pattern in any way or influence their chances of survival, compared with the rest of the population, between release and recapture. Soft bodied and aquatic animals can present real problems, but most adult arthropods and snails can be marked with a spot of cellulose paint using the point of a mounted needle. The marks must be permanent for the duration of the study.

● Destructive sampling techniques are inappropriate, at least for the initial capture.

● Estimates tend to be high, particularly if the number of recaptures is low.

There are very few animal species which meet all the requirements of this technique. It can be used for some projects, provided the limitations are understood and taken into account when interpreting the data.

(b)   A multiple capture–recapture technique

Some of the limitations of the single capture–recapture method can be overcome by adopting a multiple recapture procedure. This can be used for populations that change between samples (for instance, through emigration and immigration) and will also provide an estimate with 'better' confidence limits. The simplest of the multiple catch methods is the **Bailey Triple Catch** which requires one additional step to the procedure outlined above. The second sample is captured and the number of marked individuals in it is recorded as before, but the whole sample is then marked again in a different manner (e.g. a different colour of paint) and released. Some individuals will now bear two marks. A third sample (S_3) is collected after an appropriate time interval and the number of individuals recaptured from each of the previous samples is counted.

There is no need to count the total catch this time.

The population estimate is derived from the following:—

(i) The number of individuals that were marked in the first sample and recaptured in the second, $R_{1,2}$.

(ii) The number of individuals that were marked in second sample and recaptured in the third, $R_{2,3}$.

(iii) The number of individuals that were marked in first sample and recaptured in the third, $R_{1,3}$.

The sampling procedure is as follows:—

For sample S_1, capture, mark (by the first marking method) and release the animals (as in (a) above).

For sample S_2, capture and count the number of marked individuals ($R_{1,2}$); Mark (by the second marking method) and release all the individuals in this sample.

For sample S_3, capture and record (a) those caught previously only in the first sample ($R_{1,3}$) and (b) those caught in the second sample (include any caught in all three samples in this group)—$R_{2,3}$.
Note: You do not need to count the number of unmarked individuals.

Two steps are required to estimate the population, N:

1 First estimate the population of *marked* individuals (M) from

$$M = \frac{S_2 \times R_{1,3}}{R_{2,3}} + R_{1,2}$$

2 Then use this value of M to estimate the total population N from

$$N = \frac{M \times S_2}{R_{1,2}}$$

The 95% confidence limit can be calculated from

$$N \pm \sqrt{2N(N-S_2)\left[\left(\frac{(M-R_{1,2})+S_2}{M}\right)\left(\frac{1}{R_{2,3}}-\frac{1}{S_2}\right)+\left(\frac{1}{R_{1,2}}-\frac{1}{S_2}\right)\right]}$$

PROBLEMS AND LIMITATIONS

● There are fewer limitations than for the single recapture procedure but this method is more time consuming.

● It still assumes that marked individuals mix randomly with the remainder of the population and that they are in no way influenced by their mark.

● It assumes that all individuals will react in the same way to being captured and marked. This is a problem with small mammals, some of whom regard traps as a source of food and shelter and become 'trap-happy': others become 'trap-wary' ('trap shy') and are seldom recaptured. We have already advised against projects involving small mammals, but behavioural differences of this and other kinds may affect estimates of population size based on baited trapping.

(c)   Removal sampling

This method provides an alternative way of obtaining a rough estimate of the total number of individuals in a population in cases where it proves difficult or impossible to use mark–release–recapture techniques. A series of samples are taken, but the animals are not returned to the population at that time. Because of this, the population size diminishes with repeated sampling, and the size of each successive sample should also diminish. Depending on the method of capture, it may be possible to keep the animals alive and return them to their habitat later.

The initial population size can be estimated from the sizes of the successive samples and there are several mathematical models for obtaining such estimates. The simplest one uses data from two successive samples only. If the number caught in the first sample is S_1 and the number caught in the second sample is S_2, a rough estimate of the total population N is given by:—

$$N = \frac{S_1{}^2 - S_2}{S_1 - S_2}$$

PROBLEMS AND LIMITATIONS
- The samples must be obtained by the same method (e.g. they must be taken during identical time intervals, and there must be no bias to the second sample due to improvements in your technique).
- The method is not suitable for very large or dense populations, where the second sample may be very similar in size to the first (and sometimes even bigger!).
- This method also assumes there has been no immigration, emigration (= escape) or other changes between samples. It is only really appropriate for a closed habitat, such as an isolated pond.
- The result is only a rough estimate of total numbers.

3.3.4   Direct estimates of relative abundance

When you wish to compare populations of a species at different sites, a measure of the relative (rather than total) numbers is often sufficient. A wider range of sampling techniques is available because it is not necessary to return all the individuals unharmed to their habitat. Destructive sampling methods can be used, such as pitfall traps designed to kill the catch (Section 3.4.3). You will, however, need to devise an appropriate sampling strategy to ensure that your estimates of relative numbers are comparable between the two sites. For passive trapping techniques, the number of individuals caught 'per trap per unit time' can be recorded, whilst for active hunting techniques, such as kick sampling or sweep netting (see Section 3.4), the number caught per 'unit effort'—a combination of time and your activity— can provide a suitable measure for comparison.

Sometimes it is easier to weigh the catch than attempt to count the individuals. For instance, if you wished to study the activity pattern of midges over a period of several hours by comparing the number taken in a light trap (see Section 3.4.2), it would be much quicker to weigh the catch at the end of each half-hour period than to separate it out and count the individuals. Provided larger insects, such as moths, are removed, the weights will give an accurate measure of changes in relative abundance.

PROBLEMS AND LIMITATIONS
- The problem of achieving comparable samples should not be underestimated: samples from two sites may differ not only because the actual numbers of individuals differ but also because the technique works more efficiently at one site than the other.
- Techniques that rely on your activity often improve with practice and this can give a bias to the numbers collected in later samples. Note that the reverse may apply after a large number of replicates, as interest wanes and fatigue sets in.

3.3.5   Indirect estimates of relative abundance

Sometimes evidence of animal activity can provide an indication of relative numbers. For example, the frass (insect faeces) falling onto the woodland floor may indicate the relative abundance of caterpillars feeding in the canopy. If a sheet is left under trees or bushes for a set period of time, the accumulated frass may be weighed or counted in 'frass-units'. By enclosing some caterpillars on a convenient shoot of the same tree within a polythene bag, the frass production per insect per unit of time can be determined and the data from the sheet used to estimate the grazing intensity per unit area of canopy. Numbers of the holly leaf miner, *Phytomyza ilicis*, can be estimated from the damage they cause to holly leaves or from the number of emergence holes they leave in the leaves.

PROBLEMS AND LIMITATIONS
- These methods usually provide only a very rough indication of the relative numbers.
- A good knowledge of the behaviour of the animals being studied is necessary to avoid making unwarranted assumptions when linking the observed evidence of activity to the number of individuals.

3.4   Techniques for catching mobile organisms

This Section outlines some techniques suitable for collecting samples of mobile organisms (usually animals) from different habitats. It is intended to suggest ideas rather than provide recipes and you will probably have to adapt and develop the basic concepts to suit the conditions of your own project.

3.4.1 Invertebrates and free-floating plants in aquatic habitats: marine, estuarine and freshwater

Advice on the precautions you should adopt when working on and beside water is given on p. 23.

Various baited traps can be used to trap animals. As with quadrat sampling it is important to use the same technique throughout. For example, do not change the choice of baits between samples. Most collecting, however, is done with unbaited nets.

There is a very wide range of possible net types, but the most commonly used are tow-nets (for plankton studies), hand nets (for use in shallow water) and drift nets (to catch material washing down a stream). For all these, the size and shape of the net and its frame, together with the mesh size used, are critical.

Emergence traps located on the water's surface can be used to sample 'hatching' from the nymphal or pupal stages.

Nets

Mesh size determines the size range of the material retained in the bag. You might reasonably expect to catch more small organisms using a smaller mesh size. However, fine nets are more easily clogged and a net can only work effectively if the volume of water entering the net mouth can pass out easily between the meshes. Otherwise, the water will flow round the net rather than through it. It is necessary to use a coarser mesh in muddy water than in clear. It is a common error to try to tow fine-mesh **plankton nets** too fast, and to use too fine a mesh for the water flow in drift nets. In general, a mesh size of 1–2 mm will retain most larger invertebrates but for plankton nets 300 μm may be more suitable (roughly equivalent to 30 denier tights material) although you may need to use an even smaller mesh (e.g. 80 μm) for some studies. It is important to carry out a pilot study, using nets of different mesh sizes, before embarking on your project. But remember not to disturb your intended study area.

Appendix II includes a source of different mesh netting.

The **net frame** may be circular, D-shaped or rectangular. The choice is often a matter of personal preference, although most people use tow-nets with a circular frame and drift nets with a rectangular one. If it is necessary to be able to calculate the volume of water that has been filtered by the net these two shapes have obvious advantages. D-shaped, or other 'flat-ended', frames are most suitable for collecting bottom-living animals because they find it more difficult to escape under the frame. It is a good idea to reinforce or protect the edges of any net that will be used for bottom sampling (e.g. a shrimping net).

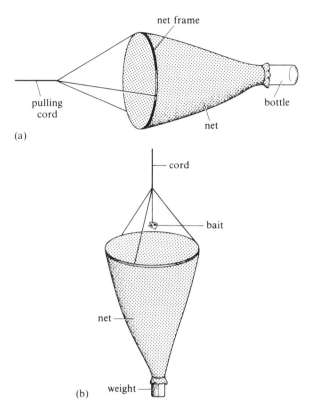

Figure 21. (a) A tow-net for collecting plankton (and everything else suspended in the water). (b) A baited drop-net for catching bottom-living carnivores.

The **shape** of the net is, naturally, influenced by the shape of the frame, but is usually a bag or cone. Drift and plankton nets usually have a collecting bottle attached to the apex of the cone (Figure 21(a)).

The **size** of your net is also a matter of convenience. Plastic sieves (sold as flour sieves) can be useful in small pools and small shallow streams. The larger the net mouth the more animals can be caught but a commercial shrimp net, with a D-shaped frame two metres across, would be impractical in a small stony hill stream! Similar considerations will influence the length of handle you want on a hand-net. The longer the pole the greater your reach but the more awkward the net will be to use (and carry).

The catch from a fine-mesh net will include many microscopic organisms invisible to the naked eye and, unless you have a field microscope with you, the whole catch must be taken home for examination. Larger invertebrates may be identified and counted in the field before being returned to their habitat. The best way of doing this is to invert the net into clean water in a white collecting dish ('family-size' ice-cream containers do very well). Individuals that prove difficult to identify can be kept in sample bottles or jars for later examination. White plastic teaspoons, broad-mouthed pipettes (e.g. a length of plastic tubing with a rubber bulb on one end) and fine paintbrushes are very useful for sorting.

Nets can be used to collect:—

(a)   Plankton

A circular-mouthed conical tow-net, often with a collecting jar attached (Figure 21a) may be towed (slowly!) from a boat or be allowed to stream in the current of a river. You may be able to wade through shallow water pulling a tow-net beside you or using a fine-mesh bag on a hand net. Sample size depends on the amount of water that passes through the net, so it is important to standardise the 'effort' used when collecting comparable samples. Planktonic plants (phytoplankton) are generally smaller than the animals (zooplankton) that feed on them and, whilst both are collected in the same manner, smaller mesh sizes usually retain a higher proportion of the plant component.

(b)   Nekton

The larger invertebrates of freshwater ponds that can swim sufficiently strongly to avoid a plankton net may be caught using a 1–2 mm mesh hand net. Make a series of sweeps through the water at the required depth, giving the net a sharp twist at the end of each stroke to retain the catch and prevent the net inverting.

(c)   Benthos

Various designs of baited trap can be used to catch bottom-feeding carnivores. Simple **drop nets** (Figure 21b) can be effective. A version intended to catch prawns from a boat or sea wall is operated by hoisting a baited net from the sea-bed. The frame is usually made from an old bicycle wheel with the spokes removed. Bait (e.g. rotting fish) is suspended over the mouth of the weighted net which is dropped to the bottom and collapses flat onto the substratum. It is left in position for several minutes to allow the victims to approach the bait, and is then hauled rapidly to the surface. A coarse (10 mm) mesh is suitable for crabs and prawns, but the design could be adapted to catch a wide variety of aquatic carnivores.

Several variants of **disturbance sampling** can be used to dislodge invertebrates living under stones or in gravel. In shallow still or slow-moving water with a stony bottom, stones can be lifted and transferred quickly into a submerged net. They are then wiped or scrubbed (as appropriate) to dislodge any invertebrates, which are collected in the underlying net.

In running water this technique can be adapted to make use of the flow. A rectangular or D-framed hand-net is pushed into the substrate and a selected number of stones are lifted

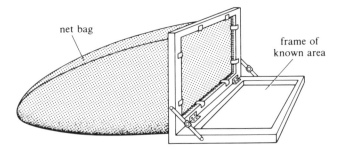

Figure 22.   A simple design of Surber sampler. In use, the horizontal frame is placed on the bed with the mouth of the net facing upstream. This sample area of substrate is disturbed so that all animals dislodged are trapped in the net.

from the water in such a way as to ensure that all the animals dislodged from them are washed into the net. **Kick sampling** is used when the substratum is composed of stones too small to be removed individually (although it can also be effective with pebbles). Position the net immediately downstream of the sampling point. Push the flat end into the substratum and disturb the bed material by kicking, scraping and churning for a timed interval (strong wellington boots advised!). A refinement of these stream collecting methods uses a **Surber sampler** (Figure 22) which limits the area sampled (effectively a quadrat frame); the bottom is disturbed with the hand or a small trowel.

In all these techniques, it is important to standardise your procedures if you wish to make realistic comparisons between sites. You should always work *upstream* when sampling at several points close together in the same body of water.

Benthic invertebrates in freshwater streams are often dislodged by the current and drift for a short distance downstream. **Drift nets,** best regarded as tow nets set across the stream bed, can be positioned so as to sample these animals. A rectangular net frame is commonly used, and the mesh size must be chosen with care to match the flow rate and the sizes of animals to be caught (see above). It is usual to empty the catch (i.e. sample) at regular intervals through a period of 24 hours. This is not a good way in which to estimate the stream fauna as a whole, but it may be useful for comparing sections of the same or different streams.

It is more difficult to catch the animals moving upstream. Rigid nets set 'the wrong way round', with the mouth facing downstream have been used and do catch animals.

Other methods of collecting aquatic invertebrates

(a)   By volume

Samples of dense plankton can be collected in bottles of

known volume at known depths in the water column. It may be necessary to sub-sample with a pipette in order to examine and count the catch under a microscope.

Animals in sandy or muddy substrata can be extracted by sieving a known volume of sand or mud in water. The organisms left in the sieve can be picked out individually, using a fine brush or forceps if necessary. The mesh size of the sieve will affect the data you obtain. When dealing with gravel samples it is best to use a combination of sieves: a wide-mesh one first to remove the larger stones followed by a fine one to retain the animals whilst letting sand and mud run away.

'Liquid mud' can be collected in a net, but more compacted sediments may be sampled with some kind of **corer** of known volume (usually an open tube forced into the sand or mud which is then withdrawn full of the substratum). All sizes have been used from **bin-samplers** (essentially a dustbin without a bottom) downwards, the size depending on the size, activity and distribution of the animals you wish to catch.

The results can be expressed as *numbers per unit volume* of substratum or as *numbers per unit surface area*. The former is applicable when the fauna is distributed more or less evenly through the sediment, the latter when most individuals are congregated near the surface.

(b) By hand

There is sometimes no alternative to searching for and picking up individuals from stones, boulders, rock surfaces and vegetation, using forceps and a wide-mouthed pipette if necessary. This method is commonly used on rocky sea shores. However, the problem of obtaining comparable samples can be particularly difficult and you must devise a standardised procedure, such as searching thoroughly over a measured area (= quadrat) or searching for a measured time interval.

(c) Using artificial substrates

When you wish to study colonisation, it is often easier to offer an **artificial substrate** rather than remove all the existing inhabitants from a natural surface. The usual procedure is to suspend plates of known size—roofing slates or pan scourers are popular—from a raft, or fix them to convenient objects. You should set up many replicates and remove a few at intervals for examination.

Trays of different substrate material may be placed on (or in) the natural bed or be suspended above it in the water body. The organisms present will colonise the artificial substrate and, after an appropriate time, the tray can be removed and the colonisers counted. This is a particularly useful method of sampling benthic animals in deeper water.

By offering a range of particle sizes, including the natural one as a control, it is possible to study habitat selection. By placing the trays at different depths you may be able to study the vertical distribution of the 'benthic' animals.

When making comparative studies it is important to standardise the length of time the artificial substrates are available for colonisation. Some organisms arrive quickly, others may require a year. Early colonisers may be replaced by later ones.

(d) Emergence trap

In cases where it is difficult to find or identify the immature stages of aquatic insects, or, when you wish to study emergence, unbaited traps can be used to capture the young adults as they rise from the water. The simplest form, is a semi-rigid net supported above a floating frame.

3.4.2 Invertebrates in the air or on vegetation

The basic instrument for handling small terrestrial invertebrates is the **pooter** (Figure 23a). This is used as an

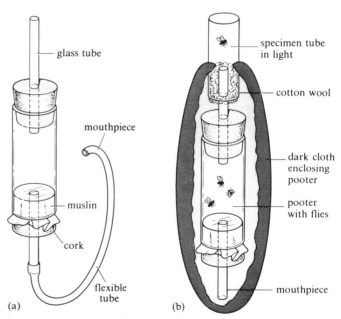

Figure 23. The insect sucking tube or **pooter.** (a) A simple design. Unless you have a large stock of pooters it will be necessary at some stage to transfer the catch to a specimen tube. (b) illustrates the best method of doing this, utilising the usual behavioural trait of insects to move towards the light. Another version of sucking pooter uses an ordinary 'glass' specimen tube and a bung with two holes through it. The idea is exactly the same as in (a) but both tubes come out of the same end of the apparatus. It requires a longer rubber tube and slightly more suck to be effective. The same bung assembly will fit many tubes so, in this case, it is the bungs that are transferred, not the catch.

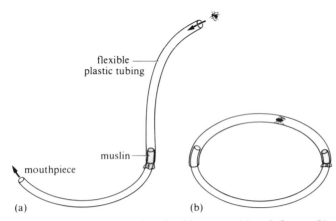

Figure 24.   A very simple design of sucking pooter: (a) ready for use; (b) closed to retain the catch.

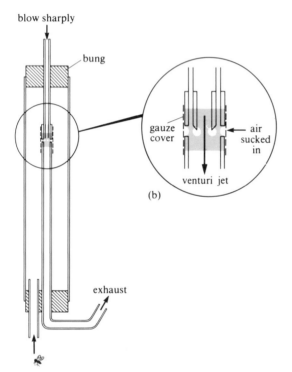

Figure 25.   A blow pooter, using the venturi effect to suck small animals in when air is blown into the mouthpiece.

aspirator; the animals are drawn up into the main chamber through the glass tube by sucking at the mouthpiece. It is essential to have at least one layer of muslin covering the inner end of the mouthpiece tube! To prevent escape out through the entrance, the upper glass tube (in the diagram) can be pushed in so that its inner end rests against the muslin below and seals the exit. A simpler version (Figure

24) consists of two lengths of plastic tubing of slightly different diameter so that the mouthpiece section fits tightly to the capture section. Again a layer of muslin should be fitted between the two. Animals can be kept in the capture section by joining the free ends, remembering to insert a second layer of muslin at this junction to prevent the catch from crawling into the mouthpiece.

Pooters can be used for collecting individual animals directly from vegetation as well as from nets and traps. Sampling rotting vegetation or dung is very unpleasant if you use the pooters illustrated in Figures 23 and 24. It is better, under these circumstances, to use a **blow pooter** (Figure 25). With this instrument, blowing down the mouthpiece creates air currents in the chamber which suck in the animals.

When you have captured your sample(s) you will need to transfer the catch to a specimen tube and, later, sort it. Most insects move towards the light and this behaviour can be used to encourage them to move from the pooter to the tube (Figure 23b). You will need fine forceps, a fine-pointed brush and several specimen tubes in order to sort the catch. Unfortunately, it is very difficult to identify small active invertebrates and it will usually be necessary to anaesthetise or kill at least a proportion of them. With small flying insects, this can be achieved easily and quickly by heat. Placing the specimen tube next to a light bulb, or even warming it in the hand, is often sufficient. Larger specimens, which are less affected by heat, may be stupefied (and eventually killed) either by placing them (in a specimen tube) in a refrigerator or in a sealed container filled with carbon dioxide. The type of cork remover that works by gas injection (using the compressed carbon dioxide in 'Sparklets' bulbs) can be used as the carbon dioxide source. If all these methods fail, you could use crushed cherry laurel leaves or you may have to resort to using a fly spray or some other killing agent. These agents are unpleasant to work with and may involve a health hazard. You should seek expert advice on their use.

There are two main approaches to the successful capture of animals: active capture and passive trapping.

For **active capture** (a–c below) you will need to plan carefully if you require comparable samples; e.g., on each occasion, search for a fixed period of time under the same weather and lighting conditions.

(a)   Kite net and Sweep net
Light-weight **kite nets** (butterfly nets) can be used for collecting flying insects above the vegetation layer. The escape of the catch can be minimised by twisting the netting

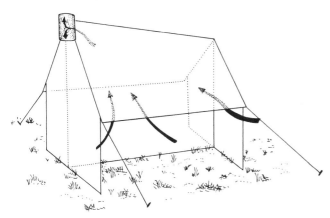

Figure 26. A malaise trap. It may be positioned at different heights above the ground to sample insects flying at different levels.

over the opening at the end of each sweep, using a figure-of-eight motion. Keep well clear of brambles and thorn bushes. **Sweep-nets** (which are more robust than kite nets) can be used to brush soft vegetation, collecting any animals resting on the plants. Interpretation of the data may not be straightforward because the catch reflects not only your activity but also that of the insects: they may be easier to catch under some conditions than others. For example, hover flies are more often collected in sweep nets by night (when they are resting on the vegetation) than they are by day, even though these are day-active insects.

(b)   Beating tray

This is the aerial equivalent of disturbance sampling and is used to capture invertebrates which live on bushes, shrubs or small trees. A white sheet is placed on the ground below the branches of the bush or shrub; if the sheet can be supported by a frame, preferably held in one hand, so much the better (an old umbrella, painted white on the inside, makes an ideal catching "tray"). The branches above it are then agitated (taking care not to cause permanent damage) to dislodge invertebrates on the twigs and foliage. Sudden taps are most successful. Spiders, mites and non-flying insects fall onto the sheet. Some flying insects are temporarily stunned and also fall down, although many will escape. The sample is collected using a pooter.

(c)   By hand

With larger invertebrates, particularly snails and slugs, there may be no alternative to sorting through the vegetation and picking up individual animals (using the fingers, forceps or a pooter according to size). It is very important to carry out a dummy run in a similar site to get your eye in before taking your samples.

Passive traps fall into two main types, those that catch the insects whilst they are in their normal flight path (d–e, below) and those that attract the animals to them by their colour, bait or light (f–i).

(d)   Sticky trap

One surface of a piece of card is smeared with a light-coloured grease and left in position (e.g. attached to a bean pole) to accumulate flying insects that blunder into it. Commercial fly-paper and fly-bands are available, but it is fairly easy to construct your own sticky traps. For flat surfaces, it is easy to smear the grease onto acetate or polythene sheets and attach these to a permanently-mounted board: used sheets can be removed and the catch sorted later. An alternative is to smear the outer surface of jam jars and to invert these on poles. The catch can be removed easily using a fine paintbrush dipped occasionally in a suitable solvent (e.g. nail varnish remover).

(e)   Malaise trap

This makes use of the well-known fact that whenever a shelter (e.g. a tent) is erected, it immediately fills with many kinds of flying insects. The malaise trap consists of a sheet of canvas or fine-mesh nylon erected like a ridge tent but with both sides held open (Figure 26). Insects entering the trap make their way upwards into the collecting bottle at the apex (which may contain a vapourised killing agent— but note the earlier warnings on the use of these agents). Water containing a drop of washing-up liquid will suffice for most short-term projects. More sophisticated versions have a series of funnels leading to the apex: insects can enter the next compartment easily but escape is made more difficult by the narrow bore of the exit. These traps are most effective in places where insects congregate naturally, such as at the edges of woods.

(f)   Water trap

Water traps are simply pale-coloured shallow dishes, or bowls, (preferably yellow or white, but you could experiment with different colours. Beware of associating the differing catches with the *colour* differences. Ultra-violet reflectance plays a large part in attractiveness to insects but cannot be detected by the human eye.) The dish is filled to a depth of about 5 mm with clear water. Day-flying insects are attracted (either by the pale colour or by the water's reflectance). A few drops of detergent added to the water cause the catch to sink and reduces the chance of the insects using the surface tension to make their way to the sides of the trap and escape. The trapped insects may be removed by forceps, a fine paintbrush or a pipette.

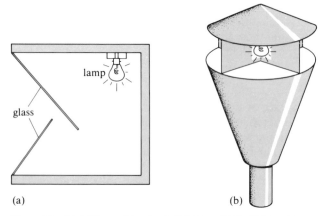

Figure 27. Light Traps: (a) a simple light box; (b) the Heistand trap.

(g) Window trap

This is used for the larger day-flying insects, such as beetles. A pale-coloured board or sheet of glass, acetate or polythene is supported upright in a frame. Flying insects hitting the board fall into a trough, containing water plus a few drops of detergent, fixed underneath. The catch is picked out as before.

(h) Light traps

Light traps are used for collecting night-flying insects. There are several designs, two of which are illustrated in Figure 27. The simplest to construct is the **light box** (Figure 27a). This may be made from an existing box by replacing one side with two glass or acetate panels placed at an angle to produce an inverted funnel shape. The other design, the **Heistand trap** (Figure 27b), uses the principle that night-flying insects approach a light source and fly round it in ever-decreasing circles. They eventually alight on the trap and fall through the funnel into the killing jar. The **Robinson trap** works on a similar principle but does not kill

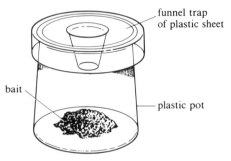

Figure 28. A baited funnel trap. Fermenting fruit as a bait would attract fruit flies, *Drosophila*.

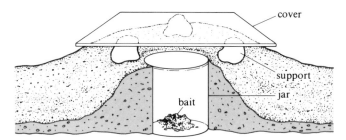

Figure 29. A baited pitfall trap. The cover is to exclude rain and larger predators.

the catch. Light bulbs that emit ultra-violet 'light' (e.g. mercury vapour lamps) usually attract more insects than ordinary bulbs. Remember that light traps catch a biased sample (that is, they attract a limited range of species and often take only the males) and that their efficiency varies with the amount of moonlight and other environmental influences on the insects.

(i) Baited funnel trap

Some insects can best be collected with baited traps. For example, fruit flies (*Drosophila*) can be attracted into a **funnel trap** (Figure 28) by a mash of fermenting banana or apple. Alternatively, the bait may be left in an exposed position and the individual flies captured by the stealthy use of a pooter. However, it is important that the same type of bait is used throughout a comparative survey.

3.4.3 Invertebrates in soil or leaf litter

These animals may be collected either *in situ* (*a* and *b* below) or be removed in a sample of the substratum from which the fauna is extracted later (*c* and *d*).

(a) Pitfall trap

Invertebrates running or crawling over the ground surface may be caught in traps sunk into the earth so as to form **pitfalls** (Figure 29). Glass jars and disposable plastic cups are convenient containers. Care should be taken so that the trap will not fill with water if it rains, and a cover of some kind also helps to exclude frogs and toads which might feed on the catch. The addition of a preservative, to kill the trapped animals, will prevent invertebrate carnivores (ground beetles and spiders) eating the rest. It also allows you to leave the trap set for several days. Diluted anti-freeze is a popular preservative, but whatever you use, remember that any such liquid may attract or repel some groups of animals and it is important to be consistent during any comparative surveys. Pitfall traps can be baited, e.g., using a fermenting bait (for flies) or a molasses and

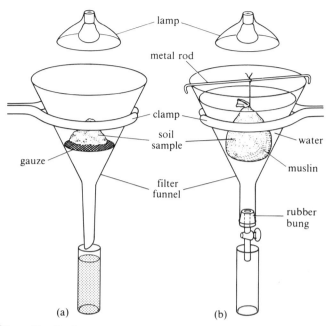

(d) Baermann funnel

This uses the same principle as the Tüllgren funnel but extracts the invertebrates living in the water film around the soil particles, rather than those that inhabit the air spaces. The soil sample is wrapped in a muslin bag and suspended in a water-filled funnel (Figure 30b). The tap at the base of the funnel allows the catch to be transferred to a specimen tube as required.

Both types of funnel should be left for several days to extract a reasonable proportion of the fauna. Some workers recommend that the funnels should be left for 24–48 hours before being placed under the light. To extract the full range of invertebrates from a soil or litter sample; first, hand sort it and then use the Tüllgren and finally the Baermann extraction methods.

3.5 Measuring environmental factors

Many ecological studies seek to relate the distribution, abundance or performance of certain organisms to particular environmental factors. This Section gives a brief outline of a range of possible techniques for recording some of the abiotic environmental factors you may wish to investigate.

Obtaining absolute measurements is often difficult and usually requires access to sophisticated equipment (such as environmental meters with light, temperature, oxygen, pH, nitrate and conductivity probes). However, it is sometimes possible to devise simple methods that give reliable and consistent readings that allow you to compare a particular abiotic factor in two or more locations, or at different times in the same location.

When trying to relate the distribution of an organism to an abiotic factor, it is important to measure that factor in the micro habitat of the organism rather than in the general environment. For example, you should measure the temperature under the leaf litter (and not in the air above) if you are studying invertebrates which live amongst decaying leaves.

3.5.1 Temperature

This is one of the easiest factors to measure, and the readings will be on an absolute scale. A **mercury-in-glass thermometer** with a thickened bulb can be used in air, soil or water (preferably in a protective case!). **Thermistor probes** connected to an appropriate meter are useful to obtain temperature measurements in places which are otherwise difficult to reach. It is important to protect all connections when using any probe in water. If you need to take measurements at different depths within the soil, it is possible to remove a small cylinder of soil using an

Figure 30. Equipment to extract very small invertebrates from soil samples: (a) Tüllgren funnel; (b) Baermann funnel. In both cases a low heat is used to drive the animals down, through the sample and so into the funnel and the collecting tube at the bottom.

beer mix which attracts molluscs. Short strips of wood, radiating outwards from the centre of the trap, can act as guides to the open hole.

(b) Chemical repellants

Earthworms may be brought to the surface by watering the ground with a dilute solution of potassium permanganate. (Household detergents can be used, but are generally less effective). Areas of grassland may be sampled using a frame quadrat procedure as in Section 3.2.2. Although not inevitable, this procedure usually kills the grass—so be careful about which sites you sample in this way.

(c) Tüllgren funnel

The **Tüllgren funnel** (Figure 30a) is used to extract small invertebrates (mostly arthropods) from samples of soil or leaf litter. The sample is placed in a funnel above a perforated disc and the whole apparatus placed under a low-powered electric light bulb. The rise in temperature and the drying effect encourage the animals to move away from the source of heat, downwards, through the holes in the perforated disc, into the funnel and so to the collecting vessel underneath. They can be collected alive, or killed by adding detergent to water in the vessel. Use a low wattage bulb—5 W—otherwise the animals will be killed by the heat before they can pass down the funnel.

extraction sampler—see Section 3.5.10—before inserting the probe.

For many studies, it is the range of temperatures over a period of time, rather than the reading at any particular moment, that is important. Standard domestic **maximum/minimum thermometers** are readily available and very useful.

3.5.2   Wind

Wind speed can be measured accurately using a **cup-anemometer,** either permanently mounted on a pole or hand held. The advantage of cup-anemometers is that they are not directional; other devices need to be orientated to the wind. A lightweight pendulum attached to a frame may be used to give comparative readings. The higher the wind speed the more the pendulum will be lifted from the vertical. A piece of card attached to the pendulum will make it more sensitive to smaller air currents. Another common design is an 'L'-shaped tube with a ball in the vertical section; you point the horizontal arm into the wind and note how high the ball rises up the vertical. Chandlers often stock such devices for sale to yachtsmen.

Wind direction can be determined by any simple **wind vane** or even a finger moistened on one side and turned very slowly in the air!
An indication of the prevailing wind direction in exposed sites is often given by the shape of trees and shrubs, which 'lean' with the wind.

3.5.3   Rainfall

A **raingauge** usually consists of a funnel of known mouth area that is held above a collecting vessel graduated to allow direct readings of rainfall, in millimetres or inches. It is easy to set up a home-made equivalent provided you know the mouth area of your funnel and relate the volume of water collected to this area. It is also possible to set a shallow, wide, vertical-sided canister part way into the ground and make direct (if approximate) measurements by reading the depth of water in the pan. This device will not record light showers and both evaporation and splash effects may present problems. It is advisable to set the rim of the canister far enough above the ground surface to prevent splash-back and flooding.

Remember to site your raingauges carefully within your study area. There may be considerable differences between gauges placed on open ground and those placed under a vegetation canopy or near buildings.

3.5.4   Relative humidity

The standard method of determining relative humidity

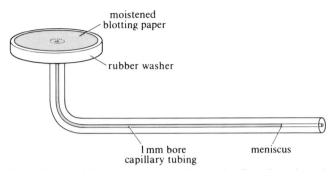

Figure 31.   A piché-type evaporimeter. Evaporation from the moistened blotting paper draws the water along the capillary tube from right to left. The rate of movement of the meniscus is a measure of the rate of evaporation.

compares the temperatures recorded by **'wet' and 'dry' thermometer** bulbs. The bulb surrounded by a wet fabric sleeve usually shows a lower temperature than the other because of the cooling effect of evaporation. The bigger the difference recorded by the two bulbs, the lower the relative humidity. There are standard tables for the conversion.

Standard wet bulb thermometers must be protected from wind (which affects the rate of evaporation) and it is usual to mount them, beside the dry bulb, within a wooden frame (Stevenson Screen). These things are not readily portable and field measurements are carried out using a **whirling hygrometer**—a wet and dry thermometer unit which is twirled in the air in much the same way as a football rattle. Other hygrometers use a coil of hygroscopic material attached to a pointer to give direct readings of humidity, but these instruments are not as accurate as whirling hygrometers.

To compare humidities in different microhabitats (such as below individual leaves), the time taken for **cobalt chloride paper** to turn from blue to pink can be recorded. You can easily prepare your own indicator paper by immersing strips of filter paper in a 5% solution of cobalt chloride and then drying them.

To compare rates of evaporation, a **piché-type evaporimeter** can be used (Figure 31). As water evaporates from the filter paper (blotting paper), the meniscus moves along the capillary tube. It is possible to adapt the design and make your own evaporimeters using straight glass capillary tubing.

3.5.5   Light

There are more problems with the measurement of light than with the measurement of any other environmental factor. Light levels fluctuate considerably, often over a short time scale, and it is very difficult to obtain meaningful values or comparisons. Plant performance and distribution is related to the total amount of light received over long periods of time, and plants may have different requirements at different times, so the light levels measured at any one moment will be of limited use. Photographic **light meters** will provide comparative readings but do not distinguish between light containing different proportions of the various wavelengths, which may be the important factor. Converting light meter readings to absolute values is not straightforward but a rough estimate may be obtained as follows:– point the light meter at a grey card (to measure reflected light). An exposure of $f16$ at $1/100$ s for 100 ASA film approximates to 750 Wm^{-2}, and each decrease in f stop (e.g. from $f16$ to $f11$) corresponds to a halving of this value.

Light probes which incorporate a cadmium sulphide cell have a sensitivity to the range of wavelengths in the visible spectrum similar to that of the absorption curves for leaves in sunlight. Note that most meters used in conjunction with light probes have logarithmic scales and they may be accurate only within a narrow range of the scale.

It is possible to compare the amount of light received over a longer period of time by using a **light sensitive paper,** such as ozalid paper used by printers, which gradually darkens when exposed to light. Pack several discs of this paper into a light-proof tube, exposing only the top one to the light. Leave the tubes at your sites for an appropriate time interval (which will depend not only on the intensity of the light but also on the type of paper used) and then extract the discs, counting the number of layers that have darkened. **Light-sensitive paint** has also been used (for example, in studies of landsnails).

Light penetration into water can be compared using a circular **Secchi disc** painted with alternate light and dark segments. It is lowered into the water until it is no longer possible to distinguish between the light and dark segments. This depth can be recorded and used for comparative readings. You must, of course, take such readings under similar lighting conditions.

3.5.6 pH

The acidity or alkalinity of the soil or water is an important factor because the presence of hydrogen ions (measured in pH readings) determines the availability of other inorganic ions to the organisms.

Care must be taken with the treatment of pH data. pH values lie on a scale from 1 (strongly acid) to 14 (strongly alkaline) and so measurements of pH are at the interval level. In most cases it is quite permissible to use statistical techniques as for any other interval level measurement, but there are problems in certain instances. For example, if you wished to calculate the pH of a solution produced by mixing equal volumes of two other solutions, one of pH 4 and the other of pH 6, then you would find that the actual pH of the mixture would be nearly 4.3 rather than the numerical mean of 5. This is because pH values are the 'negative logarithm of the hydrogen ion concentration'—so if you need to make this sort of calculation you must first convert the pH readings into values of hydrogen ion concentration $[H^+]$ (by changing the sign and taking the antilog of each pH value), take the mean of those values and then reconvert back to pH. pH measurements are one example of *transformed data* and care needs to be exercised in their treatment. Providing the distribution of the transformed values is not very skewed, it is usually not necessary to convert the data into their untransformed state before carrying out statistical procedures on them.

If you simply wish to give a general indication of the pH of the soil or water in a certain locality it would be better to indicate the *range* (highest and lowest readings recorded) instead of a mean value with standard deviation.

The pH of water samples may be measured directly using pH paper or a pH meter and probe. Soil pH is more difficult to measure. There are a number of soil-testing kits on the market (e.g. Sudbury and BDH) which include tests for pH, but these prove expensive if you wish to measure only a few samples. You may be able to obtain 'spares' of the two main reagents (universal indicator and barium sulphate solution) without having to buy the whole kit. A number of horticultural suppliers sell a simple no-battery pH probe for gardeners. The probe is inserted into damp soil; however, our tests have shown that these are not sufficiently accurate at either end of the scale to be useful for ecological studies.

It is more accurate to 'dissolve' the soil in water, and measure the pH of the 'solution' with a standard probe and meter. Take a soil sample (see Section 3.5.10) and place it in a measuring cylinder with an equal volume of distilled water. Shake it vigorously for about 10 minutes and then filter [any clay in the suspension can be flocculated if necessary by using barium sulphate solution instead of distilled water]. The pH of the filtrate is then measured. Universal indicator or pH paper can be used instead of the probe and meter, but is not as sensitive.

3.5.7 Salinity

Salinity is usually measured in parts per thousand sodium chloride (‰NaCl). The standard laboratory method of salinity determination involves silver nitrate titration, but there are two simple methods of measuring it without having to resort to this.

One is to use a **conductivity meter**. Your readings will be in ohms^{-1} (mhos) and will usually fall between the values for freshwater at around 2×10^{-4} and seawater at around 5×10^{-2}.

The other method involves a **hydrometer**, a weighted float with a graduated scale above it that indicates the density of the liquid. The instrument floats higher in denser liquids. The cheap hydrometers sold for beer-making can be very useful. There are two minor problems, (1) you need a comparatively large water sample in which to float the instrument, (2) readings are distorted by material in suspension so you must let the mud settle.

Although for comparative samples there is no need to convert the readings from either of these instruments to salinity, it is usually helpful to do so. The easiest thing is to convert all the data to percentage seawater, assuming that the water in the sea is 100% seawater, deionised or distilled water is 0% seawater and that a half-and-half mixture is 50% seawater etc.

If you can get hold of one, a direct-viewing optical **salinometer** is much quicker, but the instrument is expensive. Only a drop of the water is required and the reading is in ‰NaCl.

3.5.8   The flow rate of water

Flow meters, usually based on an impeller (a 'propeller' that is pushed by the water rather than *vice versa*) or a rotating cup system, will give direct readings and can be used to measure flow rate at various depths in the water body. The impeller blades must not touch the stream bed so these instruments cannot measure the conditions experienced by benthic invertebrates although they can record the rate of flow into a net. Flow meters are the most effective instrument in nearly all flow conditions, but they are rather delicate and very expensive.

Floats are much cheaper. Surface flow of an unobstructed stream or river is easily noted by recording the time taken for a floating object to be carried a measured distance. It is best if the object (for example, an orange) floats very low in the water so that the influence of top currents caused by wind is minimised. The fundamental problem with all floats is that surface velocity is higher than the true mean velocity so it is customary to multiply the surface velocity by 0·8 to obtain an estimate of the mean velocity. Alternatively, it may be possible to weight the float so that it travels at 0·6 of the depth (from the surface) and thus measure mean velocity—but this, of course, assumes a stream or river of constant depth.

Measurements of flow using floats give integrated values over a considerable stretch of water, and can only be used in unobstructed areas. Point measurements of surface flow may be made using **Thrupp's nails.** This device is easily constructed out of wood and consists of a 'T'-shaped

frame. Two nails, 102 mm apart and symmetrical about the midline, are half driven into the cross piece whilst the central rod carries a scale. The instrument is held with the cross-piece upstream and perpendicular to the flow so that the nails break the surface. When the velocity is greater than 0·22 ms^{-1} ripples are created. The distance, d, (in cm) from the midpoint between the nails and the farthest point of the ripples' intersection is noted. The velocity, v, (in ms^{-1}) is calculated from:—

$$v = 0·13 + 0·036d$$

The device itself is cheap, but it only works satisfactorily within a restricted range of flow rates.

Surface flow may not be the most useful measurement. A more direct measure of conditions on the stream bed uses **Hynes' volumetric method.** A plastic bag with its opening taped around one end of an open-ended tube is immersed horizontally at the chosen point, with the open end facing upstream. Record the volume collected in a set time. The flow can be calculated by dividing this volume by the cross-sectional area of the tube.

3.5.9   Oxygen levels in water

Water may be depleted of oxygen, saturated or even super-saturated. The oxygen content at saturation depends on temperature and decreases as the water temperature rises. Supersaturation occurs in turbulent streams and in places where plants are actively photosynthesising. Oxygen depletion is usually the result of the respiratory activity of organisms, often of bacteria and fungi following organic pollution.

The usual method of chemical analysis is the **Winkler Test.** This involves a sequence of reactions that produce a coloured product in proportion to the amount of oxygen present. The test is based on the reaction of manganese[IV] sulphate which forms a precipitate (manganese[II] oxide) that redissolves on adding a strong acid. When sodium iodide is added to the solution, iodine is formed in amounts determined by the amount of manganese[II] oxide. The colour of the end solution, which will range between yellow (little oxygen) to brown (fully saturated), can be compared with a colour chart and from this the oxygen content can be read off as a concentration. This can be converted to percentage saturation if the temperature is known. Winkler test kits are available commercially but note that different suppliers use slight variations in the solutions so that the colour charts are not interchangeable. More accurate measurements can be made by titrating the iodine formed against sodium thiosulphate.

The second approach is to use an **oxygen probe** and an appropriate meter which will give you a direct reading of the oxygen concentration. These are more difficult to use than most other probes and you should familiarise yourself with the instrument before attempting to collect your field data.

The procedures work well at the saturated end of the range but great care must be taken not to oxygenate samples of depleted mud or water inadvertently when trying to measure their oxygen levels.

Table 10. Key for finger assessment of soil texture. Reprinted from Burnham, C. P. (1980). The Soils of England and Wales. *Field Studies*, **5**, 349–363.

1. Does the moist soil form a coherent ball?
    Easily . . . (2)
    with great care . . . LOAMY SAND but check using tests 2 and 3
    No . . . SAND

2. What happens when the ball is pressed between thumb and forefinger?
    Flattens coherently . . . (3)
    Tends to break up . . . SANDY LOAM but check using tests 3 and 4.

3. On slight further moistening can the ball be rolled into a thick cylinder (about 5 mm thick)?
    Yes . . . (4)
    No, collapses . . . LOAMY SAND

4. On slight further moistening can the cylinder be rolled into a thin thread (about 2 mm thick)?
    Yes . . . (5)
    No . . . SANDY LOAM

5. Can the thread be bent into a horseshoe without cracking. e.g. around the side of the hand?
    Yes . . . (7)
    No . . . (6)

6. On remoulding with further moisture what is the general 'feel' of the soil?
    Smooth and pasty . . . SILT LOAM
    Rough and abrasive . . . SANDY SILT LOAM

7. Can a ring of about 25 mm diameter be formed by joining the two ends of the thread without cracking? (If necessary remould with more moisture and begin again)
    Yes . . . (9)
    No . . . (8)

8. On remoulding with further moisture what is the general 'feel' of the soil?
    Very gritty . . . SANDY CLAY LOAM
    Moderately rough . . . CLAY LOAM
    Doughy . . . SILTY CLAY LOAM

9. On remoulding without rewetting can a surface be polished with the thumb?
    Yes, a high polish like wax with few noticeable particles . . . (10)
    Yes, but gritty particles are very noticeable . . . SANDY CLAY

10. On wetting thoroughly, how strongly does the soil stick one's fingers together?
    Very strongly . . . CLAY
    Moderately strongly . . . SILTY CLAY

3.5.10 Soil (edaphic) factors

For many terrestrial projects you should provide at least a general description of the soil in your study area. Include a description of the underlying rock or the parent material, the relief, slope, and aspect of the site; also the general type of vegetation present and the land use.

The following is a very brief summary of some other assessments that can be made in addition to pH (Section 3.5.6). If your project requires detailed measurements of edaphic factors you should consult a specialist textbook.

(a) Soil depth and soil profile

Small pits can be dug (by arrangement with the landowner!) to determine the soil horizons and to record the profile. It should then be possible to identify the soil type using a key or handbook—see Appendix I.1. Alternatively, a cylinder of soil can be removed for examination using a soil auger. OU students studying S326 *Ecology* should refer to the audio cassette on soils and its related notes.

(b) Size of soil particles and soil texture

The type of soil (sand, loam or clay) is determined by the size range of the constituent particles. One way to show the proportions of different sized particles is to mix a sample with water and allow the material to settle in a graduated measuring cylinder; the larger particles (sand) settle first and the smallest (clay) last. The bands of different sized particles are clearly seen and their width can be used as a comparative measure between different sites.

A quick, but rather subjective, on-site determination of soil type uses a finger assessment (Table 10).

(c) Soil moisture

The water content of a soil changes considerably with time, so a single measurement of total water content may not be very helpful and will certainly not represent the amount available to plants.

Consider what happens when a fully-saturated soil dries out: firstly, some water will drain away—this is the

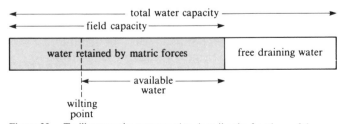

Figure 32. To illustrate the terms used to describe the fractions of the water content in a soil sample.

free-draining water (see Figure 32) which usually drains away before it can be taken up by plants. The remaining water is held around and between soil particles by **matric forces** (a combination of capillary and adhesion forces), and the maximum amount that can be so retained is the **field capacity**. 'Light' and 'heavy' soils differ in their relative capacity to retain water, which depends on such factors as the size of the soil particles, their arrangement and chemical nature. As the soil continues to dry out, matric forces increase to the point at which plants can no longer draw water from the soil and they wilt—even though some water remains. So the **available water** is the fraction between the point where all the free water has drained off and that at which most herbaceous plants wilt.

To measure the *field capacity*, you need an accurate balance, capable of weighing to within 0·1 g, and a previously saturated and drained soil sample. This latter may be obtained using a home-made **extraction sampler** as follows: trim the top of an empty tall thin can (leaving it sharp) and perforate the bottom with several holes. Drive the inverted can into the ground and remove a cylinder of soil by pulling the can out with a twisting action. This will extract a sample without compacting it too much. Immerse the sample, can and all, until it becomes thoroughly waterlogged and then allow it to drain. Weigh the sample in the can (you can subtract the weight of the can later). Now dry the sample for several hours in an oven at just over 100°C (if you use a domestic oven, select the lowest possible setting). Allow the sample to cool in a desiccator (a tin containing a small bag of silica gel will suffice), reweigh and calculate the weight differences. This is the weight of the field capacity water. You should continue drying until a constant weight is achieved.

To estimate the *available water fraction*, take a sample in the manner described above but allow it to dry out to constant weight in a desiccator at room temperature. This approximates to the point in Figure 32 where most plants start to wilt.

The water-holding properties of different soils can also be compared by placing samples in tall glass tubes (open at each end) and immersing the base in water. The water level will rise in the tube by capillary movement between the particles until it reaches a maximum height. Water rises higher in clay than in sand columns.

The **infiltration rate** is related both to soil texture and soil moisture (as well as its position on a slope and the past management of the vegetation) and can be particularly useful in studies of soil compaction (for example, the effects of trampling). Comparative data are easily taken in the field by screwing short sections of pipe (with sharpened edges) into the soil, pouring in water and recording the rate at which the water drains into the soil. All comparisons must be made at the same time as the infiltration rate depends on the amount of recent rainfall as well as drainage. Alternatively you could take a core sample of known volume, as described above, and measure how much water can pass through it in a given time.

(d) Organic content

This is determined by measuring the further loss of weight in a dry soil sample (see above) after burning-off the organic matter in a muffle furnace at 500°C. As a number of precautions are necessary (e.g. it is very important to remove all stones by careful sieving because stones can explode at 500°C!) we do not recommend attempting this unless you have access to proper laboratory facilities.

(e) Inorganic ions

Soil test kits (Sudbury or BDH) allow a very approximate measurement of selected inorganic ions. Full analysis is complex, time consuming and dependent on laboratory facilities beyond the scope of the kind of projects for which this guide is intended. The *availability* of inorganic ions present in a soil is greatly affected by pH (Section 3.5.6).

3.5.11 Biotic indices

The occurrence of certain conspicuous species can sometimes be used as a guide to the level of a particular abiotic factor. If the species concerned are long-lived, their performance represents an integration of the influence of that factor with time and may give a better assessment of its importance than can a more precise physical measurement taken on a particular day. Examples of such **indicator species** include: the lichen *Usnea articulata* which is found only at very low levels of sulphur dioxide; nettles, *Urtica dioica*, which suggest high phosphate levels in soils; and the red alga, *Corallina officinalis*, which thrives in fully-saline rock pools but is absent from brackish ones. The indicator species concept has also been used for the assessment of exposure on rocky sea shores.

Some freshwater invertebrate species are less susceptible to organic pollution and the resulting low oxygen concentrations than others—e.g. red chironomid larvae can live at very low oxygen levels whilst stonefly nymphs require high levels. **Biotic indices** for streams and rivers are calculated by giving scores for the presence of certain invertebrate taxa so that the total value indicates the 'quality' of the water. Other very useful indices have been developed, using lichens, for recognising ancient woodlands and monitoring air pollution.

3.6   Devising experiments to test your hypothesis

The methods discussed so far in Chapter 3 provide a range of techniques for collecting field data which, when analysed, will either support or cast doubt upon your hypothesis. There are instances, however, when the appropriate data cannot be collected from field observations or measurements alone. Consider again that example of moss distribution (Section 1.1). Some of the questions can be answered by collecting field data—for example, it would be possible to compare drainage rates at different sites on the lawn or to measure the association of moss with different species of grass—but others cannot be followed up in this way. If your hypothesis stated that the amount of moss was related to the quantity of cuttings left after mowing, you would have to experiment with different quantities of cuttings and subsequently measure the abundance of moss in the different sample areas.

An experimental approach is appropriate for a variety of investigations, such as relating plant growth to different fertiliser levels. With animals, you may wish to find out the *preference* shown by individuals presented with a choice of two different sets of conditions.

In experiments using a **choice chamber**, individual small invertebrates (e.g. woodlice) are placed in a container having two distinct zones (of equal area). One half might be kept dry by placing calcium chloride granules under a gauze floor and the other half moist (water under the floor). You record the location of each individual at a series of times to establish any 'preference' for one experimental condition over the other. Choice chambers for small invertebrates can be made quite easily from plastic petri-dishes. False-floors of gauze are easily inserted between the lid and base (subsequently held together with rubber bands).

The actual design of the apparatus depends on the factor you wish to investigate and scaled-up versions of this idea have been used in the field to investigate the behaviour of land snails.

Great care must be taken to ensure that the *only* difference between the two chambers is in the *single factor* to be investigated. There are two main approaches to this problem. You must either ensure that all other factors have an equal effect on both samples, or eliminate them altogether. In our moss example, the only difference between the experimental plots should be in the quantities of clippings. Randomising the location of the experimental plots over the lawn should ensure that there is no bias of 'good drainage' to the plots receiving a 'frequent cutting' treatment. With choice chambers, potential differences in light intensity between the dry and moist zones could be eliminated by carrying out the experiment in the dark.

Many successful long-term projects have involved a combination of field data collection and the use of experiments to test hypotheses. In shorter projects, it may be impossible to attempt both approaches and you must decide which is the more appropriate.

Chapter 4   Statistical techniques

Chapter 4 contains details of several statistical techniques. Before you can decide which one is best suited to your particular analysis, you have to be clear about the following:

(a) Whether you wish to make decisions about differences between the populations from which your samples come, or whether you wish to make decisions about associations between features within the population from which your sample comes (see Section 1.3.5).

(b)   whether your measurements are at the interval, ordinal or categorical level (see Section 2.2.1);

(c) whether your measurements are matched or unmatched (see Section 2.2.2).

Once you are certain about these things, consult the decision chart, opposite (also reproduced on the inside back cover) which tells you which technique you might use, and where to find it described. Then turn to the relevant Section, to discover whether the technique is, in fact, appropriate.

The layout for each of the technique Sections is the same. First, in a box, is a summary of the situations in which you may use the test. Not all of this may be clear until you have read the entire Section on the technique, but once you have done this you should read this box through again *before* carrying out the test on your own data, to check that the conditions required by the test are met.

Next the rationale of the test is discussed, in terms that are intended to appeal to your intuition, rather than to any mathematical principles.

After this there is usually a brief summary of the procedure, in symbols—useful for quick reference once you become thoroughly familiar with the technique. This is followed by a worked example, which you should find particularly useful when going through the technique for the first time. Sometimes the procedure involves alternative routes, depending, for example, on whether you are working with large or small samples.

Finally there is a list of 'Do's and Don't's, which you should work through carefully. This list should help you to avoid making the commonest errors found in research projects.

Ten statistical techniques will now be described, in Sections 4.1–4.10.

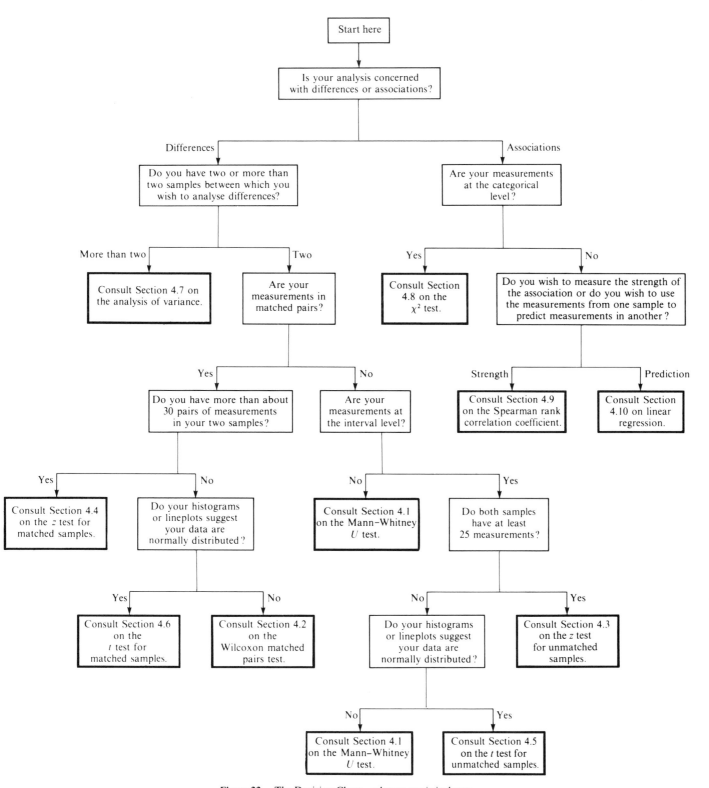

Figure 33. The Decision Chart—a key to statistical tests.

4.1   The Mann–Whitney U test

When to use

1   If you wish to test for differences in population **medians**.

2   Provided you have two **unmatched** samples.

3   Provided your data are either at the **ordinal** or the **interval** level.

4   Provided the populations from which the samples come have the **same shaped distribution** (they do *not* need to be normally distributed).

5   Do not use if **one** of the samples has **only one measurement**, or if **both** samples have **under five measurements**.

6   If your measurements are at the interval level, do not use when both sample sizes are **greater than 25.** Use the z test for unmatched samples (Section 4.3).

7   It is difficult to use the Mann–Whitney U test to calculate confidence intervals without the use of a computer.

Rationale of test

Suppose that you have two unmatched samples and that you wish to test the null hypothesis that they come from populations with the same medians. Sample A contains four measurements, which in increasing order of size are A_1, A_2, A_3 and A_4. The other sample, B, contains three which—again in increasing order of size—are B_1, B_2 and B_3. (It would be unwise in practice to use such small samples, but we chose small samples here to simplify the explanation.)

The exact values of these measurements do not matter, but you must be able to say which is the smallest, which the next smallest, and so on, ranking them all in order of increasing size.

If the null hypothesis is true, then it is unlikely that all of the measurements in sample A will be smaller than all of those in B, or vice versa—see Figure 34(a) and (b).

It is far more likely, if the null hypothesis is true, that the measurements from the two samples will overlap to some extent, as in Figure 34(c).

The Mann–Whitney U test provides a simple way of quantifying the overlap between measurements in two samples, and also tells you the probability of obtaining such an overlap if the null hypothesis is true. To measure

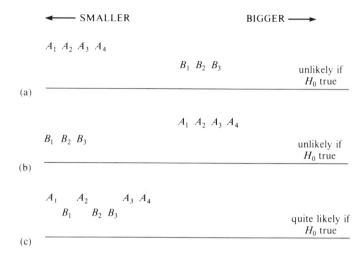

Figure 34.   Likely and unlikely outcomes of an investigation, given the null hypothesis H_0 that the two samples, A and B, come from populations with the same medians.

the overlap, start with one of the samples, take each measurement from that sample in turn and count how many measurements in the other sample are smaller than it. Keep a tally as you go along. Then swap the two samples round, and go through the procedure again. For example, with the data in Figure 34(a), you would proceed as follows. First count how many sample B measurements are smaller than each of the sample A measurements. A_1 does not have any measurements from sample B smaller than it, nor does A_2 or A_3 or A_4. So the total number of times sample B measurements are smaller than sample A measurements is zero. Now swap the two samples round, and count how many times sample A measurements are smaller than sample B measurements. B_1 has four sample A measurements smaller than it, so does B_2, and so does B_3. So the total number of times sample A measurements are smaller than sample B measurements is 12.

The situation in Figure 34(b) is the mirror image of that in Figure 34(a), and not surprisingly, if you were to go through the same procedure with these two samples, you would find that the number of times sample A data were smaller than sample B measurements was zero as well, and that the number of times sample B data were smaller than sample A data was 12.

☐   Go through the same procedure for the data in Figure 34(c).

■   Sample A:
      A_1 has 0 sample B measurements smaller than it.

A_2 has 1
A_3 has 3
A_4 has 3

total   7

Sample B:

B_1 has 1 sample A measurement smaller than it.

B_2 has 2

B_3 has 2

total   5

Notice that in examples (a) and (b), where there is no overlap between the two samples, the lower of the two totals we calculated is 0 and the higher is 12. By contrast, in example (c) where there is considerable overlap, the lower total is 5 and the higher is 7. From this it seems that, if the null hypothesis is true, we would expect the two totals to be close together, whereas if it is false we would expect them to be far apart: one very high and the other very low. This suggests that either of the pair of totals could act as a test statistic: a very high or a very low total might lead one to reject the null hypothesis. In fact, it is the smaller of the two that is used. The test statistic is usually denoted by the letter U. It is possible to work out the probability distribution of U when the null hypothesis is true, although we do not do this here. It turns out that the probability distribution is different for each different pair of sample sizes; for example, Figure 35 shows the U values obtained by taking two samples, each containing four measurements, from two populations with the same median (i.e. one sample from

each population). The calculated value of U will lie between 0 and 8 inclusive. If you take such samples repeatedly, the value of U will fluctuate from sample to sample. If the null hypothesis is true, there is a probability of about 0·2 (20%) of getting a value $U = 6$, a probability of just under 0·1 (10%) of getting a value $U = 3$, and a probability of 0·03 of getting a U value of 0. The probability of getting a U value of 1 is also 0·03, so the probability of getting a value of 1 or smaller is $0·03 + 0·03 = 0·06$, which is greater than 0·05. Hence we can reject H_0 only if $U = 0$, assuming that the criterion for rejecting H_0 is a probability of 5% or less. (Note that for the Mann–Whitney U test, unlike the test described in Section 2.4.3, we reject the null hypothesis if the test statistic is equal to or *smaller than* the critical value.)

Rather than drawing scores of probability distributions for different combinations of sample sizes, it is usual to present a Table (e.g. Table III(2) in Appendix III) of the critical values that U takes for a given significance level, for various combinations of sample size. The following example shows you how to use these Tables, and how to carry out the whole Mann–Whitney U test.

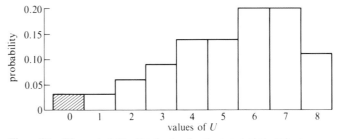

Figure 35. The probability distribution for the test statistic U for two samples, each with four measurements.

WORKED EXAMPLE

Procedure

1   Call the two samples A and B, respectively. Rank the data in the samples in increasing order of size.

Calculation

sample A: 18   19   15   23   19

sample B: 19   21   16

←SMALLER   LARGER→

sample A: 15   18   19   19   23

sample B: 16   19   21
                              (equally
                              ranked)

2   For each measurement in sample B, count how many in sample A are smaller. Write down this number. (Sometimes measurements in samples A and B will have the same value. Each time this happens, count a score of $\frac{1}{2}$.)

sample B measurement	comment	no. of sample A measurements smaller than sample B measurement
16	one sample A measurement—15—is smaller than the sample B measurement of 16	1
19	two sample A measurements—15 and 18—are smaller than the sample B measurement of 19. So they contribute a score of 2; also, two sample A measurements—19 and 19—have the same value as the sample B measurement of 19. So, score $\frac{1}{2}$ for each of them $(2+\frac{1}{2}+\frac{1}{2}=3)$	3
21	four sample A measurements—15, 18, 19 and 19—are smaller than the sample B measurement of 21	4
	total	8

3   When you have worked your way through all the measurements in the sample, add up the numbers you have written down to give a grand total. Call this U_A.

4   Carry out steps 2 and 3 again, this time with the two samples swapped around.

Therefore $U_A = 8$

sample A measurements	comment	no. of sample B measurements smaller than sample A measurements
15	no sample B measurements are smaller than 15	0
18	one measurement—16—is smaller than 18	1
19	one measurement—16—is smaller than 19 and one has the same value as 19	$1\frac{1}{2}$
19	one measurement—16—is smaller than 19 and one has the same value as 19	$1\frac{1}{2}$
23	three measurements—16, 19 and 21—are smaller than 23	3
	total	7

Call the new grand total that you get U_B.

Therefore $U_B = 7$.

5   Check that your calculations are correct in the following way. If the size of sample A is n_A and of sample B is n_B, then, if you have calculated U_A and U_B correctly, $U_A + U_B$ will equal n_A multiplied by n_B. If it does not, recalculate U_A and U_B.

$n_A = 5 \qquad n_B = 3$
$U_A = 8 \qquad U_B = 7$
$U_A + U_B = 8 + 7 = 15$
$n_A \times n_B = 5 \times 3 = 15$

Therefore $U_A + U_B = n_A \times n_B$ and the calculation is correct.

6   Choose the smaller of U_A and U_B. This is the test statistic. If one of your sample sizes is greater than 20 go to step 7. Otherwise, carry on reading.

Refer to Table III(2) which shows critical values of U at the 5% significance levels. The critical value of U for the two sample sizes is found at the intersection of the appropriate row and column. If, for example, both your sample sizes are 8 then read down from the 8 in the top row and along from the 8 in the left-hand column until the two lines meet. The critical value is 13. This means that when both sample sizes are 8, the test statistic U has to be 13 or smaller for you to be able to reject the null hypothesis at the 5% level. To take another example, if your sample sizes are 13 and 10, read down from the 13 in the top row and along from the 10 in the left-hand column until the two lines meet. The critical value of U in this case is 33. You will notice that you cannot use Table III(2) if one or both samples are very small, and indeed you are advised to ensure that both sample sizes are greater than 10 if at all possible.

Decide whether or not to reject the null hypothesis.

7 Table III(2) (a standard Table of critical values for the test statistic U) can only cope with sample sizes of up to 20. If one of your samples is larger than this proceed as follows.

If n_A and n_B are the two sample sizes, and U is the test statistic, calculate a new test statistic called z, as follows.

$$z = -\frac{U - (n_A n_B/2)}{\sqrt{n_A n_B (n_A + n_B + 1)/12}}$$

For example, let $U = 154$, $n_A = 18$ and $n_B = 25$.
Then

$$z = -\frac{154 - (18 \times 25/2)}{\sqrt{18 \times 25 \times (18 + 25 + 1)/12}} = -\frac{-71}{40 \cdot 6202} = 1 \cdot 74790$$
$$= 1 \cdot 75 \text{ (to two decimal places)}$$

The probability distribution of z is very well known (it is the standard normal distribution—see Section 4.3) and it is therefore possible to calculate critical values of z for various significance levels; three values are given in Table 11.

Table 11 Critical values of z for three significance levels.

significance level:	5%	1%	0·1%
critical value for z:	1·96	2·58	3·29

You can reject the null hypothesis at a given level of significance only if the absolute value of your calculated z (ignoring any minus signs) is *greater* than or equal to the critical value. In the present example, the calculated value of z is 1·75, which is smaller than 1·96, so the null hypothesis cannot be rejected at the 5% significance level.

Do's and Don't's for Mann–Whitney U tests

1 The Mann–Whitney U test is designed to be used on unmatched samples. Do not, therefore, carry out such a test on matched pairs of measurements.

2 The test is based on the assumption that the measurements in the two populations (from which the samples are taken) have the same shaped distribution, like Figure 36a and b and unlike Figure 36c. Although you cannot produce histograms for your populations, you *can* do so for your samples. Your samples will probably be too small to be very informative, but if the shapes of their distributions appear to be widely different, do not use the Mann–Whitney U test.

3 Since it is a test for differences in population **medians,** do not use the Mann–Whitney U test to make statements about population *means*. This is a common error; for example, one often comes across statements such as: 'The *mean* of sample A was $\overline{x}$, and of sample B was $\overline{y}$. A Mann–Whitney U test showed that these differed significantly at the 5% level.'

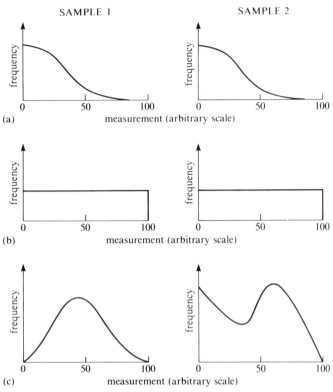

SAMPLE 1   SAMPLE 2

(a)   measurement (arbitrary scale)

(b)   measurement (arbitrary scale)

(c)   measurement (arbitrary scale)

Figure 36. Pairs of samples from populations with distributions that are (a and b) and are not (c) the same.

4   If your measurements are at the interval level and both your sample sizes are greater than 25, do not use the Mann–Whitney U test. It is quicker and easier, in such circumstances, to use the z test (see Section 4.3).

4.2   The Wilcoxon matched pairs test

When to use
1   If you wish to test for differences in population **medians**.
2   Provided you have two **matched** samples.
3   Provided that your measurements are at the **interval level**.
4   Provided that the differences between matched measurements from the two samples are **symmetrically distributed**.
5   Do not use if the number of non-zero differences between matched measurements is **less than 5** or **greater than 30**.
6   It is difficult to use the Wilcoxon matched pairs test to calculate confidence intervals without the use of a computer.

Rationale

Suppose that you have two matched samples, and that you wish to test whether they come from populations with the same medians. Sample A contains four measurements: A_1, A_2, A_3 and A_4. Sample B also contains four measurements: B_1 matched with A_1, B_2 matched with A_2, B_3 matched with A_3 and B_4 matched with A_4. (Note that, although we call the measurements A_1, A_2, A_3 and A_4, we are *not* saying that these are ranked in order of size—that A_1 is the smallest and A_4 the largest, for example. A_1 is simply the first measurement that you made in sample A, and B_1 is the measurement from sample B with which (following the principles explained in Section 2.2.2) A_1 is matched.) For the purposes of this test, you have to know how big the measurements are; that is, the measurements need to be at the interval level. This means that it is possible to calculate how far apart the two measurements are in each matched pair: you can calculate the difference between A_1 and B_1, between A_2 and B_2, and so on.

If the null hypothesis that population medians are equal is true, it is unlikely that all of the measurements in sample A will be smaller than those in B, or vice versa; that is, it is unlikely that:

$$A_1 > B_1 \qquad A_2 > B_2 \qquad A_3 > B_3 \qquad A_4 > B_4$$

or that

$$A_1 < B_1 \qquad A_2 < B_2 \qquad A_3 < B_3 \qquad A_4 < B_4$$

It is more likely, if the null hypothesis is true, that some of the measurements from sample A will be larger than their matched measurements from sample B, and that some will be smaller; for example:

$$A_1 > B_1 \qquad A_2 < B_2 \qquad A_3 > B_3 \qquad A_4 < B_4$$

Consider now the *size* of the difference between each matched pair of measurements. Some of the sample A measurements may be much bigger than their matched sample B measurements, some only slightly bigger. Similarly, some of the sample B measurements may be much bigger than their matched sample A measurements, and some only slightly bigger. If the null hypothesis is true, then it is unlikely that all of the big differences will be in one direction and all of the small ones in the other; for example, the following result is unlikely:

A_1 much bigger than B_1 $\qquad$ A_2 just smaller than B_2
A_3 much bigger than B_3 $\qquad$ A_4 just smaller than B_4

It is more likely, if the null hypothesis is true, that there will be as many big differences and as many small differences in one direction as in the other; for example:

A_1 much bigger than B_1 $\qquad$ A_3 just bigger than B_3
A_2 much smaller than B_2 $\qquad$ A_2 just smaller than B_4

The idea behind the Wilcoxon matched pairs test is to sort differences only according to their various magnitudes, and to see whether any trend is apparent—whether big differences occur in one direction and small differences in the other, or whether both are more or less equally common in each direction. To do this, it is necessary to rank all of the differences in order of increasing size.

EXAMPLE 1

Consider the pair of matched samples, each containing six measurements of leaf length, in columns 2 and 3 of Table 12. The smallest difference is between measurements A_6 and B_6, a difference of only 1 (see column 4) so this gets a rank of 1 in column 5. The next smallest difference is between measurements A_2 and B_2, a difference of 2, so this gets a rank of 2. The largest difference is between A_3 and B_3, a difference of 9, so this gets a rank of 6. We do not, at this stage, take into account whether the differences are positive or negative.

Table 12 Matched samples, for Example 1.

(1) measurement no.	(2) sample A	(3) sample B	(4) difference (A minus B)	(5) rank
	leaf length/cm			
1	8	12	-4	4
2	9	7	$+2$	2
3	12	3	$+9$	6
4	6	9	-3	3
5	14	6	$+8$	5
6	10	11	-1	1

The ranking procedure has told us the size of the differences between matched measurements, but has not told us in which directions they occur. To discover this, divide the ranks you have just calculated into two groups: those that are associated with positive differences, and those that are associated with negative ones. In the present example, this produces the following result:

measurement no.	rank	direction of difference
1	4	$-$
2	2	$+$
3	6	$+$
4	3	$-$
5	5	$+$
6	1	$-$

The result is perhaps clearer if positive and negative differences are set out in two separate columns:

ranks of positive differences	ranks of negative differences
2	4
6	3
5	1
total 13	total 8

If the null hypothesis is true, you would expect the sum of the ranks of the negative differences to be roughly equal to the sum of the ranks of the positive differences. You would not expect them to be wildly different. In the present

Table 13 Matched samples, for Example 2.

measurement no.	sample C	sample D	difference (C minus D)/mg	rank of difference	ranks of positive differences	ranks of negative differences
	seed weights/mg					
1	10	20	-10	5		5
2	11	12	-1	1		1
3	14	23	-9	4		4
4	13	15	-2	2		2
5	13	26	-13	6		6
6	21	24	-3	3		3
					total 0	total 21

example, the sum of the negative differences is 8 and of the positive differences is 13, which is some way from equality, but not enormously so.

EXAMPLE 2

Consider another example, which is of two matched samples of seed weights (Table 13). Here, all of the differences are negative and there are no positive differences at all. As a result, the sum of the ranks of the positive differences, 0, is much smaller than that of the negative differences, 21. It is unlikely that you would get such large differences in these totals if the null hypothesis were true.

EXAMPLE 3

Try to do this example yourself:

☐ Table 14 shows two matched samples of relative humidity. The null hypothesis is that the samples come from populations with equal medians. Calculate the sum of the ranks of the positive differences and of the negative differences. Are you likely to get such totals if the null hypothesis is true?

■ First find the differences, and rank them, as in Table 15. The two totals are very close together, a result that is very likely if the null hypothesis is true.

Table 16 summarises the pairs of totals that we have calculated in the last three examples, and the conclusion that can be drawn in each case about the null hypothesis. The Table bears out the statement made earlier that if the null hypothesis is true, you would expect the sum of the

Table 14 Matched samples, for Example 3.

measurement no.	relative humidity/%	
	sample E	sample F
1	57	64
2	49	54
3	53	51
4	50	54
5	57	51
6	56	48

ranks of the positive and negative differences to be roughly equal rather than to be wildly different.

The results in the Table suggest that either of the sums could act as a test statistic. The test statistic is usually denoted by the letter W. It is not difficult to work out from first principles the probability distribution of W given that the null hypothesis is true, but we do not do this here.

It turns out that the probability distribution of W is different for each pair of sample sizes. You can work out the critical value of W from Figure 37 for a 5% significance level. If two samples, each containing six measurements, come from populations with the same median, the calculated value of W will lie between 0 and 21 inclusive (since $6+5+4+3+2+1=21$). If you take such samples repeatedly, the value of W will fluctuate from sample to sample. If the null hypothesis is true, there is a probability of about 0·03 (i.e. 3%) that W will be as extreme as 0 or 21.

Table 15 The ranks of the differences for Example 3.

measurement no.	relative humidity/%		difference (E minus F)/%	rank of difference	ranks of positive differences	ranks of negative differences
	sample E	sample F				
1	57	64	−7	5		5
2	49	54	−5	3		3
3	53	51	+2	1	1	
4	50	54	−4	2		2
5	57	51	+6	4	4	
6	56	48	+8	6	6	
					total 11	total 10

Table 16   Sums of positive and negative differences in Examples 1, 2 and 3.

	Example 1	Example 2	Example 3
sum of positive differences	13	0	11
sum of negative differences	8	21	10
likelihood of obtaining such sums if H_0 true	moderate	low	high

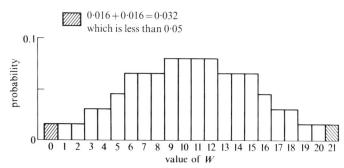

Figure 37.   The probability distribution of W, the test statistic for the Wilcoxon matched pairs test, when both samples contain six measurements.

Hence if we obtain a value for W of 0 or 21, we can reject the null hypothesis at the 5% level.

Rather than drawing several probability distributions for different sample sizes, it is usual to present a Table of critical values for W for given significance levels (see Table III(3) in Appendix III). To use this Table, first choose whichever of the two sums of differences (positive or negative) is the smaller for your test statistic W.

WORKED EXAMPLE

Procedure

1   Arrange the measurements from the two samples in matched pairs side by side (columns 1 and 2).

2   Subtract each measurement for sample B from its paired measurement in sample A (column 3).

3   Ignoring whether the differences are positive or negative, rank the differences in increasing order of size (column 4). The smallest difference should be given rank 1, the next smallest rank 2, and so on. Differences of equal magnitude should be given an average rank. Thus the two differences of 4 share the average rank of 4·5.

If two matched measurements have the same value, so that the difference between them is zero, remove them altogether from the calculations.

4   Divide the ranks into two groups: those associated with positive differences, and those associated with negative differences.

5   Add up the ranks in each of the two groups.

Calculation

(1) sample A	(2) sample B	(3) difference (A minus B)	(4) rank of differences
16	12	+4	4·5
15	15	0	—
10	14	−4	4·5
9	10	−1	1
7	5	+2	2
17	14	+3	3
8	13	−5	6

Remove the measurements of 15 and 15 from the calculations.

ranks of positive differences, R^+	ranks of negative differences, R^-
4·5	4·5
2	1
3	6
total 9·5	total 11·5

$$R^+ = 9.5, \qquad R^- = 11.5$$

6   Check the accuracy of your calculations as follows. Let R^+ be the sum of the positive ranks and R^- the sum of the negative ones. Let the number of differences that are not zero be N_D.

Then, if your calculations are correct, you will find that

$$R^+ + R^- = \tfrac{1}{2}N_D(N_D + 1)$$

If it does not, re-do your calculations.

7   Choose the smaller of R^+ and R^-, and let this be the test statistic W.

Refer to Table III(3) in Appendix III which shows critical values of W at various significance levels and N_D values. Reject the null hypothesis only if the calculated value of W is equal to or *smaller* than the critical value given in the Table for your chosen level of significance and calculated value of N_D. (Note that the Table does not give critical values for N_D values less than 5, so it is not worth carrying out the test with matched samples with fewer than five non-zero differences.)

$N_D = 6$

(There are 7 pairs of measurements, and hence 7 differences (A minus B), but one of these is zero, so $N_D = 6$.)

$$9 \cdot 5 + 11 \cdot 5 = \tfrac{1}{2} \times 6(6 + 1)$$
$$21 = 3 \times 7 = 21$$

$R^+ = 9 \cdot 5$ $R^- = 11 \cdot 5$

Therefore $W = 9 \cdot 5$

At the 5% significance level for $N_D = 6$, the critical value of $W = 0$.

W is greater than this, so do not reject H_0.

Do's and Don't's for the Wilcoxon matched pairs test

1   The Wilcoxon matched pairs test can only be used on **matched** samples. Do not, therefore, carry out such a test on unmatched samples.

2   The test is based on the assumption that the differences in measurements taken from the two populations are symmetrically distributed. Figure 38 shows some symmetrical distributions. Notice that the distribution of the differences does not have to be normal, but it does have to be symmetrical. In practice, you will usually be working with small samples (see point 3 below), and even if you were to plot frequency distributions of your differences, it would be very difficult to discover whether they were symmetrically distributed or not. Most people therefore work on the assumption that the differences *are* symmetrically distributed, unless there are good reasons for supposing the contrary.

3   Do not use the test for sample sizes of more than 30. The test becomes increasingly cumbersome with large sample sizes, and there are quicker tests that can be used on large samples (see Section 4.4).

4.3   The z test for unmatched samples

When to use

1   If you wish to test for differences in population **means**.

2   Provided you have two **unmatched** samples.

3   Provided that your measurements are at the **interval** level of measurement.

4   Provided that your samples have **at least 25** measurements each.

Rationale

Suppose that you have two unmatched samples, each containing 25 or more measurements, and that you wish to test whether they came from populations with the same means. The example of crampon shells given in Section 2.4 would be suitable here, and much of the rationale behind the z test is described in that Section. For the z test to be

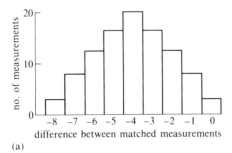

(a)

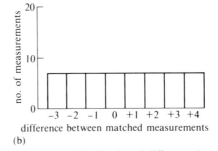

(b)

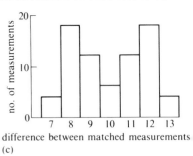

(c)

Figure 38.   Three examples, each showing a symmetrical distribution of differences between matched pairs of measurements.

valid, your measurements must be at the interval level: lengths, weights, durations and other common biological measurements fall into this category.

Suppose that you have two samples of crampon shells, A and B, which come respectively from populations with mean shell lengths of μ_A and μ_B. (The Greek letter μ, pronounced mu to rhyme with new, is the symbol commonly used to denote a population mean.) The null hypothesis H_0 would be that the mean shell lengths of the two populations were the same, and the alternative hypothesis H_1 would be that they were different. In symbols these hypotheses could be written as:

$$H_0: \quad \mu_A = \mu_B$$

$$H_1: \quad \mu_A \neq \mu_B$$

Another way of writing the null hypothesis is:

$$H_0: \quad \mu_A - \mu_B = 0$$

That is, if $\mu_A = \mu_B$, then the difference in population means is zero.

You know from Section 2.4.1 that if you repeatedly take pairs of samples from populations A and B and calculate the difference in sample means for each pair, then, if the null hypothesis is true, these differences will be clustered around a mean value of zero and will be normally distributed.

If the differences in sample means are normally distributed, we know that about two-thirds of them will lie within one standard error from the mean, about 95% within two, and that we can calculate the percentage of differences that lie within any chosen number of standard errors from the mean. All that you have to do, therefore, is to find out how many standard errors away from the mean is the difference in sample means that you have calculated. Taking the crampon example in Section 2.4.1, the standard error of the difference in sample means was 2·772 mm. If the difference in means of two shell samples happened to be 2·772 mm, this would be exactly one standard error from the mean difference of zero; if the difference happened to be 4·200 mm, this would be 4·200/2·772 = 1·515, or roughly 1·5 standard errors from the mean, and so on. Figure 39 illustrates this.

Figure 39(b) is especially important because it shows the shape of the normal distribution that you get when you express your difference in sample means as 'so many standard errors from their mean'. It is called the **standard normal distribution.** Figure 39(b) tells us that about 13% of differences in sample means are more than 1·5 standard errors away from their mean. Thus under the null hypothesis that our two samples of shells come from populations with the same mean length, the probability of

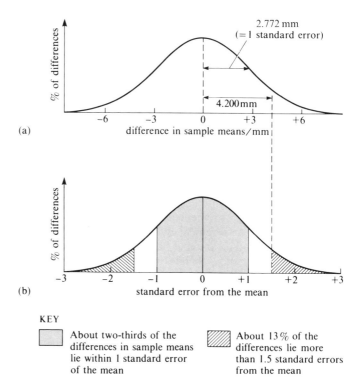

KEY

About two-thirds of the differences in sample means lie within 1 standard error of the mean	About 13% of the differences lie more than 1.5 standard errors from the mean

Figure 39.   Differences in sample means (a) the difference in sample means for the shell example in Section 2.4.1. and; (b) the same differences expressed in terms of standard errors of the mean.

obtaining a difference in sample means of at least 1·5 standard errors is 13%. This is considerably greater than the value of 5% or less that we require, to be able to reject the null hypothesis; so we would accept it.

The preceding paragraphs present the essence of the *z* test. In it, you *convert* your difference in sample means to a new number: the number of standard errors your difference lies from the mean difference expected under the null hypothesis. This new number, the test statistic, denoted by the letter *z*, has a normal probability distribution with a mean of zero and a standard deviation of 1. There are Statistical Tables (see Table 11 on p. 54, for an example) that give critical values of *z* for tests at various levels of significance. The critical values can also be used to calculate confidence intervals (see the worked example opposite).

To put the above into symbols:

Let two samples, A and B, have means of $\bar{x}_A$ and $\bar{x}_B$ respectively. Let the standard error of the difference in sample means be SE_D. Then the difference in sample means is $\bar{x}_A - \bar{x}_B$, and the number of standard errors this difference lies from zero, denoted by *z*, is given by:

$$z = \frac{\bar{x}_A - \bar{x}_B}{SE_D}$$

One final problem remains. Given two samples A and B, say of crampon shells, it is easy to calculate their respective means $\bar{x}_A$ and $\bar{x}_B$; but how do we discover the standard error of the difference in the sample means?

As Section 2.4 showed, it is impossible to collect all possible pairs of samples from the two populations of shells, and to work out from them the distribution of all differences in mean sample lengths. Instead, you have to *estimate* the standard error of the difference in sample means, and you do this from the measurements in your two samples. If sample A has n_A measurements with a sample standard deviation of s_A, and if sample B has n_B measurements with a standard deviation of s_B, then it turns out that the

estimated standard error for the difference in sample means SE_D is given by

$$SE_D = \sqrt{\frac{s_A{}^2}{n_A} + \frac{s_B{}^2}{n_B}}$$

But $z = \dfrac{\bar{x}_A - \bar{x}_B}{SE_D}$

Thus, substituting for SE_D,

$$z = \frac{\bar{x}_A - \bar{x}_B}{\sqrt{\dfrac{s_A{}^2}{n_A} + \dfrac{s_B{}^2}{n_B}}}$$

from which z can be calculated.

WORKED EXAMPLE

Procedure

Calculation

1   Arrange your sample measurements x_A and x_B in two columns (columns 1 and 3) and work out the sample mean and variance of each, using the procedure given in Section 2.3.3, or a suitable computer program.

Consider two samples of crampon shells, A and B.

(1) sample A	(2)	(3) sample B	(4)
shell length x_A/mm	$x_A{}^2$	shell length x_B/mm	$x_B{}^2$
60·3	3 636·09	57·2	3 271·84
61·9	3 831·61	56·9	3 237·61
59·8	3 576·04	58·1	3 375·61
58·7	3 445·69	55·0	3 025·00
61·1	3 733·21	56·3	3 169·69
60·7	3 684·49	54·1	2 926·81
62·4	3 893·76	55·5	3 080·25
58·1	3 375·61	56·0	3 136·00
58·9	3 469·21	54·2	2 937·64
60·0	3 600·00	55·8	3 113·64
59·7	3 564·09	53·9	2 905·21
59·9	3 588·01	55·1	3 036·01
62·1	3 856·41	54·9	3 014·01
61·1	3 733·21	55·4	3 069·16
60·3	3 636·09	54·3	2 948·49
61·2	3 745·44	53·9	2 905·21
		53·2	2 830·24

Following the procedure in Section 2.3.3:

(i) Square each measurement from each sample, to give $x_A{}^2$ and $x_B{}^2$, and enter them in columns 2 and 4.

(ii) Add up the numbers in each column, to give Σx_A, $\Sigma x_A{}^2$, Σx_B and $\Sigma x_B{}^2$.

$\Sigma x_A = 966 \cdot 2$ $\Sigma x_A{}^2 = 58\,368 \cdot 96$ $\Sigma x_B = 939 \cdot 8$ $\Sigma x_B{}^2 = 51\,982 \cdot 42$

(iii) Divide the totals of the measurements by the sample size, n_A or n_B, to give the sample means. (note that in order to simplify calculations we are using sample sizes of less than 25 here, whereas in practice this should not be done.)

$$\frac{\Sigma x_A}{n_A} = \frac{966 \cdot 2}{16}$$

$$= 60 \cdot 3875$$

(this is the mean of sample A, $\bar{x}_A$)

$$\frac{\Sigma x_B}{n_B} = \frac{939 \cdot 8}{17}$$

$$= 55 \cdot 2824$$

(this is the mean of sample B, $\bar{x}_B$)

(iv) Square the totals of the measurements

$$(\Sigma x_A)^2 = 966 \cdot 2^2$$
$$= 933542$$

$$(\Sigma x_B)^2 = 939 \cdot 8^2$$
$$= 883224$$

(v) Divide each of the figures you have just calculated by the corresponding sample size to give $(\Sigma x_A)^2/n_A$ and $(\Sigma x_A)^2/n_B$

$$\frac{(\Sigma x_A)^2}{n_A} = \frac{933542}{16} = 58346 \cdot 4$$

$$\frac{(\Sigma x_B)^2}{n_B} = \frac{883224}{17} = 51954 \cdot 4$$

(vi) subtract the figures from step (v) from the totals of the squared measurements, (Σx_A^2 and Σx_B^2)

$$58368 \cdot 96 - 58346 \cdot 4$$
$$= 22 \cdot 56$$

$$51982 \cdot 42 - 51954 \cdot 4$$
$$= 28 \cdot 02$$

(vii) Divide each of the figures from step (vi) by one less than the corresponding sample size

$$\frac{22 \cdot 56}{16 - 1} = \frac{22 \cdot 56}{15}$$
$$= 1 \cdot 504$$

$$\frac{28 \cdot 02}{17 - 1} = \frac{28 \cdot 02}{16}$$
$$= 1 \cdot 751$$

(viii) These figures are the sample variances, s_A^2 and s_B^2.

$$s_A^2 = 1 \cdot 504$$

$$s_B^2 = 1 \cdot 751$$

2   Calculate the estimated standard error of the difference between the sample means, SE_D using the equation

$$SE_D = \sqrt{\frac{s_A^2}{n_A} + \frac{s_B^2}{n_B}}$$

$$SE_D = \sqrt{\frac{1 \cdot 504}{16} + \frac{1 \cdot 751}{17}}$$

$$= \sqrt{0 \cdot 094 + 0 \cdot 103}$$

$$= 0 \cdot 443847$$

3   Calculate *z*, using the equation

$$z = \frac{\bar{x}_A - \bar{x}_B}{SE_D}$$

$$z = \frac{60 \cdot 3875 - 55 \cdot 2824}{0 \cdot 443847}$$

$$= 11 \cdot 5019$$

$$= 11 \cdot 50 \text{ (to two decimal places)}$$

4   Choose which of the following you require:

(i) a significance test: if so, go to step 5.
(ii) a confidence interval: if so, go to step 6.

5   The value of *z* that you have calculated may be either positive or negative. This will depend upon which of your two samples you decide to call sample A, and which sample B. This is an arbitrary decision—if in the worked example you had reversed the labels on the two samples, your calculated value of *z* would have been − 11·50

mean of sample A = 55·2824

mean of sample B = 60·3875

SE_D = 0·443847 (as before)

$$z = \frac{55 \cdot 2824 - 60 \cdot 3875}{0 \cdot 443847}$$

$$= -11 \cdot 5019$$

$$= -11 \cdot 50 \text{ (to two decimal places)}$$

Absolute value of *z* = 11·50

Take the absolute value of *z*, ignoring whether it is positive or negative, and compare it with critical values for *z* (z_{crit}) at various levels of significance. The critical values are as follows:

significance level:	5%	2%	1%	0·1%
z_{crit}	1·96	2·33	2·58	3·29

If your calculated value of z is greater than or equal to a critical value, you can reject H_0 at the corresponding significance level.

6   The most usual confidence interval to calculate is the 95% confidence interval for the difference in population means. You may, however, choose other confidence intervals if you wish.

(i)   Choose from the following list the appropriate critical value of z:

confidence interval:	95%	99%	99.9%
z_{crit}	1.96	2.58	3.29

(ii)   Calculate the difference in sample means.

(iii)   The lower limit of the confidence interval is given by
$$(\overline{x}_A - \overline{x}_B) - (z_{crit} \times SE_D)$$

(iv)   The upper limit of the confidence interval is given by
$$(\overline{x}_A - \overline{x}_B) + (z_{crit} \times SE_D)$$

(v)   So the confidence limits are given by
$$(\overline{x}_A - \overline{x}_B) \pm (z_{crit} \times SE_D)$$

11.50 is greater than 3.29, so we can reject H_0 at the 0.1% level of significance in favour of the alternative hypothesis.

For this worked example, we choose a 95% confidence interval, for which the critical value of z is 1.96.

$$\overline{x}_A - \overline{x}_B = 60.3875 - 55.2824$$
$$= 5.1051 \text{ mm}$$

lower limit
$$5.1051 - (1.96 \times 0.443847)$$
$$= 5.1051 - 0.869940$$
$$= 4.23516$$
$$= 4.24 \text{ mm (to two decimal places)}$$

upper limit
$$5.1051 + (1.96 \times 0.443847)$$
$$= 5.1051 + 0.869940$$
$$= 5.97504$$
$$= 5.98 \text{ mm (to two decimal places)}$$

The 95% confidence interval in the worked example is 4.24 mm to 5.98 mm.

Thus we estimate, with 95% confidence, that the difference between the population means lies between 4.24 and 5.98 mm.

Do's and Don't's for z tests for unmatched samples

1   The z test, as described here, can only be used on **unmatched** samples. Do not, therefore, use this test on matched samples. A different version, which can be used on matched samples, is described in Section 4.4.

2   Your measurements should be at the interval level, but they need *not* be normally distributed. (This is because the means from large samples of the same population will be approximately normally distributed, even though the individual measurements from the population may not be.)

3   Do not use the z test if your samples are small. As a rough guide, both sample sizes should be at least 25. If your measurements appear *not* to be normally distributed (and frequency distributions will help you to decide this) use sample sizes well over 25.

4   When deciding how large your samples should be, consider the following points:

(i)   Larger samples give better indications of the populations from which they come than do smaller ones, so from one point of view, the bigger the samples, the better. But—

(ii)   There is a law of diminishing returns. For example, an increase in sample size from 25 to 35 might alter the value of the test statistic z considerably, whereas an increase from 125 to 135 would have less effect.

Thus, although large samples provide a sounder basis for making inferences about populations, it may not be worth while working with very big samples. Here, practical considerations come into play. How difficult, expensive, or time consuming is it to collect your measurements? Could you better spend your time on extending your project in other directions, rather than collecting very big samples to answer just one question? These are matters for your own judgement, and for discussion with your tutor or teacher.

4.4   The *z* test for matched samples

When to use

1   If you wish to test for differences in population **means**.

2   Provided you have two **matched samples**.

3   Provided your measurements are at the **interval** level.

4   Provided that you have **at least 30 measurements** in **each** of your two **samples**.

Rationale

First read the rationale behind the *z* test for unmatched samples (Section 4.3). The *z* test for matched samples is a simple extension of the unmatched test. Imagine that you have two matched samples A and B of say 30 measurements each, with the measurements at the interval level, and that you wish to test whether they come from populations with identical means. In symbols,

$$H_0: \quad \mu_A = \mu_B$$

Suppose that you now calculate the difference between each pair of measurements, by subtracting one from the other. If the null hypothesis is true, you would expect that some differences will be positive and some negative but that on average they will be close to zero, as seems probable from the early part of Table 17. By contrast, if the average is far

Table 17   Likely outcomes for differences in paired measurements from samples A and B, if H_0 (that population means are equal) is true.

measurement no.	sample A	sample B	difference (A–B)
1	A_1	B_1	D_1 (+ve)
2	A_2	B_2	D_2 (+ve)
3	A_3	B_3	D_3 (−ve)
4	A_4	B_4	D_4 (−ve)
5	A_5	B_5	D_5 (+ve)
.	.	.	.
.	.	.	.
.	.	.	.
30	A_{30}	B_{30}	D_{30} (−ve)

Table 18   Unlikely outcomes for differences in paired measurements from samples A and B if H_0 is true.

measurement no.	sample A	sample B	difference (A–B)
1	A_1	B_1	D_1 (+ve)
2	A_2	B_2	D_2 (+ve)
3	A_3	B_3	D_3 (+ve)
4	A_4	B_4	D_4 (+ve)
5	A_5	B_5	D_5 (+ve)
.	.	.	.
.	.	.	.
30	A_{30}	B_{30}	D_{30} (+ve)

from zero, as in the early part of Table 18, then H_0 is unlikely to be true. In fact, under the null hypothesis, you expect the mean of the differences to be zero, and, moreover, that the mean differences will be normally distributed around zero with a certain standard error (SE_D). The rationale of the *z* test applied to matched pairs is, therefore, to calculate the mean of the differences, and to discover how many standard errors away from zero this mean lies. This gives the *z* statistic, which can be treated in the same way as for unmatched samples.

WORKED EXAMPLE

Procedure

1   Arrange your sample measurements in two columns (2 and 3), with the matched pairs on the same row (e.g. 14 and 16 in row 3 are a matched pair). Subtract each sample B measurement from its matched sample A measurement, writing the answer in column 4.

Calculate the sample mean and variance of the differences in column 4, using the procedure given in Section 2.3.3. Following that procedure

(i)   Square each difference in column 4, and put the results in column 5.

Calculation

(1) measurement no.	(2) sample A	(3) sample B	(4) difference (A − B)	(5) difference squared
1	13	10	+3	9
2	15	12	+3	9
3	14	16	−2	4
4	20	15	+5	25
5	21	16	+5	25
6	18	20	−2	4
7	11	10	+1	1
8	11	15	−4	16
9	21	17	+4	16
10	19	10	+9	81
.	.	.	.	.
.	.	.	.	.
.	.	.	.	.
30	14	17	−3	9
		total*	45	328

(ii)   Add up the numbers in columns 4 and 5.

This gives

$\Sigma(A - B)$ and $\Sigma(A - B)^2$.

*Most of sample measurements are not shown, for the sake of brevity. The totals are for *all* the sample measurements, both those that are shown and those that are not.

$\Sigma(A - B) = 45$ $\Sigma(A - B)^2 = 328$

(iii) Divide the total in column 4 by the sample size. The number you have calculated is the mean of the differences between matched pairs of measurements, $\overline{D}$.

$$\Sigma(A - B)/n = 45/30$$
$$= 1\cdot5$$
$$\overline{D} = 1\cdot5$$

(iv) Square the total of column 4 to give $(\Sigma(A - B))^2$

$$(\Sigma(A - B))^2 = 45^2$$
$$= 2025$$

(v) Divide the figure from step (iv) by the sample size to give $(\Sigma(A - B))^2/n$

$$(\Sigma(A - B))^2/n = 2025/30$$
$$= 67\cdot5$$

(vi) Subtract the figure from step (v) from the total of column 5 to give $\Sigma(A - B)^2 - (\Sigma(A - B))^2/n$

$$\Sigma(A - B)^2 - (\Sigma(A - B))^2/n$$
$$= 328 - 67\cdot5$$
$$= 260\cdot5$$

(vii) Divide the figure from step (vi) by one less than the sample size

$$\frac{\Sigma(A - B)^2 - (\Sigma(A - B))^2/n}{n - 1} = \frac{260\cdot5}{29}$$
$$= 8\cdot98276$$

(viii) This is the sample variance of the differences in the paired measurement, $s_D{}^2$.

$$s_D{}^2 = 8\cdot98276$$

2   Calculate the estimated standard error of the mean differences in paired measurements, SE_D, using the equation

$$SE_D = \sqrt{\frac{s_D{}^2}{n}}$$

where n is the sample size.

$$SE_D = \sqrt{\frac{8\cdot98276}{30}} = 0\cdot547198$$

3   Calculate *z* using the equation

$$z = \frac{\overline{D}}{SE_D}$$

$$z = \frac{1 \cdot 5}{0 \cdot 547198}$$
$$= 2 \cdot 74124$$
$$= 2 \cdot 74 \text{ (to two decimal places)}$$

4   For a significance test go to step 4 of the *z* test for unmatched samples, and for a confidence interval go to step 6. Proceed exactly as for unmatched samples.

Do's and Don't's for *z* tests for matched samples

The *z* test, as described here, can only be used on matched samples. Do not, therefore, use it on unmatched samples. The other do's and don'ts are the same as for the unmatched *z* test, see Section 4.3.

4.5   The *t* test for unmatched samples

When to use

1   If you wish to test for differences in population **means**.

2   Provided you have two **unmatched** samples.

3   Provided that your measurements are at the **interval** level.

4   When your samples are small; that is when one or both have **fewer than 25** measurements.

5   Provided that the measurements can be assumed to come from **normally** distributed populations with **equal variances**.

Rationale

First, make sure that you are familiar with the rationale of and the procedure for the *z* test for unmatched samples (Section 4.3). You will notice that the *z* test can only be used when the sample sizes are large—each containing 25 or more measurements.

If you have smaller samples than this, which often happens in biological research, then you cannot use the *z* test. Recall that the equation for calculating *z* is

$$z = \frac{\overline{x}_A - \overline{x}_B}{SE_D}$$

where the difference in sample means, $\overline{x}_A - \overline{x}_B$, is assumed to be normally distributed, and SE_D is the estimate of the standard error of the difference in means. It turns out that

with small samples there are two problems. First, $\overline{x}_A - \overline{x}_B$ will not be normally distributed unless the populations from which the samples come are themselves normally distributed. (Remember that with large samples, $\overline{x}_A - \overline{x}_B$ will be normally distributed, whether or not the parent populations are normally distributed.) Second, the method of estimating SE_D [the standard error of the differences in sample means] used in the *z* test is not appropriate when small samples are used. So with small samples the *z* test cannot be used, and the *t* test is used instead.

The *t* test differs from the *z* test in certain important respects to cope with the problems just mentioned. First, you use a different method of estimating SE_D. Second, you calculate your test statistic, *t*, using the equation

$$t = \frac{\overline{x}_A - \overline{x}_B}{SE_D}$$

and compare this, not with critical values obtained from the normal distribution, but with critical values obtained from a different probability distribution. We shall consider these two points in more detail.

(i)   Calculating SE_D

First, we have to make one major assumption, which is that the two populations from which the samples come have the same variance. This is usually called the **common population variance,** and is denoted by S_C^2. Suppose that you wish to estimate S_C^2 from two samples: sample A containing n_A measurements and with a sample variance of s_A^2, and sample B containing n_B measurements and with a sample variance of s_B^2. (You can calculate these sample variances using the method in Section 2.3.3, or by using appropriate programs.)

Then the estimate of the common population variance is given by

$$S_C^2 = \frac{(n_A - 1)\, s_A^2 + (n_B - 1)\, s_B^2}{(n_A - 1) + (n_B - 1)}$$

From this, you can calculate SE_D from the equation:

$$SE_D = \sqrt{\frac{S_C^2}{n_A} + \frac{S_C^2}{n_B}}$$

You then use this value of SE_D to find the value of t, using:

$$t = \frac{\bar{x}_A - \bar{x}_B}{SE_D}$$

(ii)   The sampling distribution of t

Unlike the test statistic z, the sampling distribution of t varies with the sample size. More precisely, it varies with what is called the number of **degrees of freedom**. To obtain the number of degrees of freedom, you subtract 1 from each sample size, and add the two resulting numbers together. So, if the two sample sizes are n_A and n_B, the number of degrees of freedom is $(n_A - 1) + (n_B - 1)$. (Another way of writing this is $n_A + n_B - 2$.) Thus the number of degrees of freedom is slightly smaller than the combined size of both samples. Figure 40 shows the sampling distribution of t for various degrees of freedom. It also shows the standard normal distribution, for comparison. You can see that if the number of degrees of freedom is small, the distribution of t is flatter and more widely spread than the standard normal distribution: a larger area of the distribution lies towards the extremes in the t distribution than in the standard normal distribution. So critical values of t for a given level of significance have to be larger than corresponding critical values of z. You will also notice that when the number of degrees of freedom is large, the distribution of t comes closely to resemble that of z. This is one reason why, with large samples, you can use the simpler z test rather than the t test.

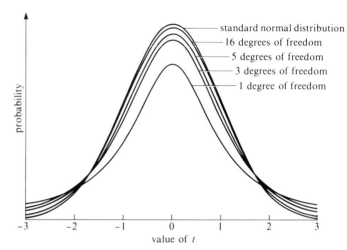

Figure 40. The sampling distribution of the test statistic, t, for various degrees of freedom, compared with the normal distribution.

The implication of this Figure 40 is that when you wish to discover the critical value of t for a given significance level, you have to take the number of degrees of freedom into account. There are Statistical Tables (e.g. Table III(4)) that give critical values of t for various significance levels and for different numbers of degrees of freedom. The following example shows how to use these Tables.

WORKED EXAMPLE

Procedure

1   Arrange your sample measurements in two columns, and work out the sample mean and variance of each, using the procedure given in Section 2.3.3 or a suitable program.

(i)   Square each measurement in each sample (columns 2 and 4)

Calculation

Consider two samples of leaf weights, A and B

(1) Sample A	(2)	(3) Sample B	(4)
Weight/grams		Weight/grams	
x_A	$x_A{}^2$	x_B	$x_B{}^2$
3·0	9·00		
4·6	21·16	1·9	3·61
2·8	7·84	3·1	9·61
4·1	16·81	3·3	10·89
2·5	6·25	2·8	7·84
5·0	25·00	3·8	14·44
3·2	10·24	3·7	13·69
3·4	11·56	3·4	11·56

(ii)   Add up the numbers in each column.

$\Sigma x_A = 28\cdot 6$ $\Sigma x_A{}^2 = 107\cdot 86$ $\Sigma x_B = 22\cdot 0$ $\Sigma x_B{}^2 = 71\cdot 64$

(iii) Divide each of the totals of the measurements by the sample size

$$\frac{\Sigma x_A}{n_A} = \frac{28 \cdot 6}{8}$$
$$= 3 \cdot 5750$$

$$\frac{\Sigma x_B}{n_B} = \frac{22 \cdot 0}{7}$$
$$= 3 \cdot 1429$$

These are the means of samples A and B, $\overline{x}_A$ and $\overline{x}_B$ respectively.

$$\overline{x}_A = 3 \cdot 5750$$

$$\overline{x}_B = 3 \cdot 1429$$

(iv) Square the totals of the measurements to give $(\Sigma x_A)^2$ and $(\Sigma x_B)^2$

$$(\Sigma x_A)^2 = 28 \cdot 6^2$$
$$= 817 \cdot 96$$

$$(\Sigma x_B)^2 = 22 \cdot 0^2$$
$$= 484 \cdot 0$$

(v) Divide each of the figures from step (iv) by the corresponding sample size to give $(\Sigma x_A)^2/n_A$ and $(\Sigma x_B)^2/n_B$

$$(\Sigma x_A)^2/n_A = 817 \cdot 96/8$$
$$= 102 \cdot 245$$

$$(\Sigma x_B)^2/n_B = 484/7$$
$$= 69 \cdot 1429$$

(vi) Subtract the figures from step (v) from the totals of the squared measurements to give $\Sigma x_A^2 - (\Sigma x_A)^2/n_A$ and $\Sigma x_B^2 - (\Sigma x_B)^2/n_B$

$$\Sigma x_A^2 - (\Sigma x_A)^2/n_A$$
$$= 107 \cdot 86 - 102 \cdot 245$$
$$= 5 \cdot 615$$

$$\Sigma x_B^2 - (\Sigma x_B)^2/n_B$$
$$= 71 \cdot 64 - 69 \cdot 1429$$
$$= 2 \cdot 4971$$

(vii) Divide each of the figures from step (vi) by one less than the corresponding sample size

$$\frac{5 \cdot 615}{8 - 1} = \frac{5 \cdot 615}{7}$$
$$= 0 \cdot 802143$$

$$\frac{2 \cdot 4971}{7 - 1} = \frac{2 \cdot 4971}{6}$$
$$= 0 \cdot 416183$$

(viii) These figures are the sample variances $s_A{}^2$ and $s_B{}^2$

$$s_A{}^2 = 0 \cdot 802143$$

$$s_B{}^2 = 0 \cdot 416183$$

2 Calculate the estimated common population variance from the equation

$$S_C{}^2 = \frac{(n_A - 1)\, s_A{}^2 + (n_B - 1)\, s_B{}^2}{(n_A - 1) + (n_B - 1)}$$

[Notice that the two numbers added together on the top of the fraction defining $S_C{}^2$ are the two numbers calculated in step 1(vi) during the calculation of the sample variances]

$$S_C{}^2 = \frac{(7 \times 0 \cdot 802143) + (6 \times 0 \cdot 416183)}{(8 - 1) + (7 - 1)}$$
$$= \frac{5 \cdot 615 + 2 \cdot 4971}{13}$$
$$= 0 \cdot 6240$$

3   Calculate the estimated standard error of the difference in sample means from the equation:

$$SE_D = \sqrt{\frac{S_C{}^2}{n_A} + \frac{S_C{}^2}{n_B}}$$

$$SE_D = \sqrt{\frac{0 \cdot 6240}{8} + \frac{0 \cdot 6240}{7}}$$
$$= \sqrt{0 \cdot 0780 + 0 \cdot 0891}$$
$$= 0 \cdot 40878$$

4   Calculate *t* from the equation:

$$t = \frac{\overline{x}_A - \overline{x}_B}{SE_D}$$

$$t = \frac{3 \cdot 5750 - 3 \cdot 1429}{0 \cdot 40878}$$
$$= 1 \cdot 05705$$
$$= 1 \cdot 057 \text{ (to three decimal places)}$$

5   Calculate the number of degrees of freedom,

$$= (n_A - 1) + (n_B - 1)$$

No. of degrees of freedom

$$= (8 - 1) + (7 - 1) = 13$$

6   Choose which of the following you require:

(i) A significance test: if so, go to step 7.

(ii) A confidence interval: if so, go to step 8.

7   The value of *t* you have calculated may be positive or negative, depending upon which of your two samples you decided to call sample A, and which sample B. Take the absolute value of *t* (that is, ignore whether *t* is positive or negative).

The value of *t* would either be 1·057 or − 1·057, depending on which sample you called A and which B.

The absolute value of *t* is 1·057.

Refer to Table III(4) of Appendix III, which shows critical values of t at various significance levels.

If H_0: $\mu_A = \mu_B$

and H_1: $\mu_A \neq \mu_B$

then reject H_0 in favour of H_1 at a given level of significance if your calculated value of t is bigger than the critical value of t for that significance level.

From Table III(4), the critical value of t for 13 degrees of freedom at the 5% significance level is 2·160. The calculated value of t, 1·057, is smaller than this, so H_0 cannot be rejected.

8   The most usual confidence interval to calculate is the 95% confidence interval. You may, however, choose other confidence intervals if you wish.

(i) Select from Table III(4) the value of t appropriate to the confidence interval of your choice and to the number of degrees of freedom.

We choose a 95% confidence interval, and there are 13 degrees of freedom. Therefore,

$t = 2·160$

(ii) Calculate the difference in sample means.

$\bar{x}_A - \bar{x}_B = 3·575 - 3·1429 = 0·4321$

(iii) The lower limit of the confidence interval is given by

$(\bar{x}_A - \bar{x}_B) - (t \times SE_D)$

and we calculated $(\bar{x}_A - \bar{x}_B)$ in step 8(ii), t in step 8(i) and SE_D in step 3.

Lower limit

$0·4321 - (2·160 \times 0·40878) = 0·4321 - 0·882965$

$\qquad = -0·450865$

$\qquad = -0·45 \text{ g (to two decimal places)}$

(iv) The upper limit of the confidence interval is given by

$(\bar{x}_A - \bar{x}_B) + (t \times SE_D)$

Upper limit

$0·4321 + (2·160 \times 0·40878) = 0·4321 + 0·882965$

$\qquad = 1·31507$

$\qquad = 1·32 \text{ g (to two decimal places)}$

(v) So the confidence interval is given by

$(\bar{x}_A - \bar{x}_B) \pm (t \times SE_D)$

The 95% confidence interval in the worked example is:

$-0·45$ g to $+1·32$ g

This signifies that we can be 95% confident that the mean of the population from which the sample was drawn is no more than 1·32 g greater than, and no more than 0·45 g less than, the mean of the population from which sample B was drawn.

Do's and Don't's for *t* tests for unmatched samples

1   The t test, as described here, can only be used on unmatched samples. An alternative version for matched samples is described in Section 4.6.

2   Your measurements must be at the interval level and must be **normally distributed**. With small samples it is very difficult to discover whether the populations from which they come are in fact normally distributed. You should, however, draw line plots or histograms of the measurements in your two samples. If they appear to be very skewed, then do not use the t test: use medians and the Mann–Whitney U test instead (Section 4.1).

Most biological measurements involving weights, lengths, volumes and areas, etc. are not normally distributed. Only those relating to even-aged stands of plants and discrete age-classes of animals are likely to fit that distribution. Be careful also when working with measurements, such as percentages, where it may be theoretically impossible for a measurement to exceed or be smaller than a particular value. For example, a researcher might measure the percentages of mosquitos killed by two brands of insecticide, A and B in two sets of 50 trials. Histograms of the results might be as in Figure 41. Most of the mosquitoes are killed by both brands, but the researcher might still wish to test whether the mean percentages were different. You clearly cannot get more than 100% of the mosquitoes killed in any one trial, so you end up with very irregularly-shaped distributions, with most of the measurements clustered just below 100% and a drop to

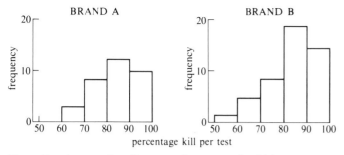

Figure 41. An example to illustrate a circumstance in which *t* tests cannot be used: the results from (hypothetical) experiments on two brands of insecticide.

zero above 100%. A *t* test would be inappropriate in such a case. Instead, you should test for a difference in population medians using a Mann–Whitney *U* test.

3   The variances of the populations from which your samples come should be equal. Again it is difficult to find out whether this is the case if you have small samples, because the variances of small samples even if taken from populations with equal variances can fluctuate widely. It turns out, however, that differences in the variances of the two populations do not severely affect the value of *t* provided that the two samples are roughly equal in size, so it is worth keeping your sample sizes as close to each other as possible.

4   When both sample sizes are over 25 (and hence with 48 or more degrees of freedom), use the *z* test rather than the *t* test.

4.6   The *t* test for matched samples

> **When to use**
> 1   If you wish to test for differences in population **means**.
> 2   Provided that you have two **matched** samples.
> 3   Provided that your measurements are at the **interval** level.
> 4   When your samples are small; that is when each sample has **fewer than about 30** measurements.
> 5   Provided that the measurements can be assumed to come from **normally** distributed populations.

Rationale

The rationale for this test is very similar to that for the *z* test for matched samples. Before reading any further make sure that you understand the rationales for the *z* test for matched samples, and for the *t* test for unmatched samples.

Just as the *t* test (rather than the *z* test) must be used on small unmatched samples, the same applies to small matched samples. Imagine that you have two matched samples of, say, 10 measurements each, with measurements at the interval level, and that you wish to test whether they come from populations with the same mean. In symbols

$$H_0: \quad \mu_A = \mu_B.$$

As in the *z* test for matched samples, you calculate the difference between each matched pair of measurements by subtracting one from the other. If the null hypothesis is true, you would expect the mean of the differences, $\overline{D}$, to be zero, with a standard error SE_D. For large samples, you can calculate the test statistic *z* from:

$$z = \frac{\overline{D}}{SE_D}$$

For small samples, you have to calculate the test statistic *t*, using the same equation:

$$t = \frac{\overline{D}}{SE_D}$$

Here, as in the *t* test,

$$SE_D = \sqrt{\frac{s_D^2}{n}}$$

Summary

$\overline{D}$ = mean difference between pairs of sample measurements

n = number of measurements in each sample

s_D^2 = variance of differences in paired measurements

$$t \quad = \frac{\overline{D}}{SE_D} \text{ where } SE_D = \sqrt{\frac{s_D^2}{n}}$$

Compare the calculated value of *t* with the critical value, for $n-1$ degrees of freedom.

WORKED EXAMPLE

Procedure

1   Arrange your sample measurements in two columns (2 and 3), with each matched pair on the same row. Subtract each sample B measurement from the corresponding sample A measurement, and put the answers in column 4.

Calculate the mean, $\overline{D}$, of the differences in column 4. Also, calculate the variance of the differences in column 4, $s_D{}^2$, using the procedure given in Section 2.3.3 or a suitable program. Following the procedure in Section 2.3.3:

(i) Square each difference in column 4 and put the result in column 5.

Calculation

(1) measurement no.	(2) sample A	(3) sample B	(4) difference (A − B)	(5) difference squared (A − B)^2
1	16	12	+4	16
2	15	15	0	0
3	18	13	+5	25
4	17	18	−1	1
5	19	11	+8	64
6	18	15	+3	9
			totals:	
			19	115

(ii) Add up the numbers in each of columns 4 and 5, to give $\Sigma(A-B)$ and $\Sigma(A-B)^2$ respectively.

$$\Sigma(A-B) = 19 \qquad\qquad \Sigma(A-B)^2 = 115$$

(iii) Divide the total of column 4 by the sample size n. This number is $\overline{D}$, the mean of the differences between paired measurements

$$\frac{\Sigma(A-B)}{n} = \frac{19}{6} = 3\cdot1667$$

$$\overline{D} = 3\cdot1667$$

(iv) Square the total in column 4 to give $(\Sigma(A-B))^2$

$$(\Sigma(A-B))^2 = 19^2 = 361$$

(v) Divide the figure from step (iv) by the sample size to give $(\Sigma(A-B))^2/n$

$$\frac{(\Sigma(A-B))^2/n}{n} = \frac{361}{6} = 60\cdot1667$$

(vi) Subtract the figure you have just calculated in (v) from the total of column 5 to give $\Sigma(A-B)^2 - (\Sigma(A-B))^2/n$

$$\Sigma(A-B)^2 - (\Sigma(A-B))^2/n = 115 - 60\cdot1667$$
$$= 54\cdot8333$$

(vii) Divide the figure from step (vi) by one less than the sample size

$$\frac{\Sigma(A-B)^2 - (\Sigma(A-B))^2/n}{n-1}$$
$$= \frac{54\cdot8333}{6-1} = \frac{54\cdot8333}{5}$$
$$= 10\cdot9667$$
$$s_D{}^2 = 10\cdot9667$$

(viii) This is the sample variance of the difference in paired measurements, $s_D{}^2$.

2   Calculate the estimated standard error of the mean difference in paired measurements, using the equation:

$$SE_D = \sqrt{\frac{s_D{}^2}{n}}$$

$$SE_D = \sqrt{\frac{10\cdot9667}{6}} = \sqrt{1\cdot82778} = 1\cdot35195$$

3   Calculate t using the equation:

$$t = \frac{\overline{D}}{SE_D}$$

$$t = \frac{3\cdot16667}{1\cdot35195} = 2\cdot34230$$
$$= 2\cdot342 \text{ (to three decimal places)}$$

4   Calculate the number of degrees of freedom, $n-1$.

$$n - 1 = 6 - 1 = 5$$

5   Go to step 6 of the t test for unmatched samples and proceed exactly as for unmatched samples (p. 69).

Do's and Don't's for *t* tests for matched samples

1   The *t* test, as described here, can only be used on matched samples. Do not use it, therefore, on unmatched samples.

2   When the number of degrees of freedom exceeds about 30, you can use the matched pairs *z* test instead, since the two tests give virtually identical results.

3   Your measurements need to be at the interval level and to be normally distributed. (Strictly, it is the population of differences between paired measurements that needs to be normally distributed.) In practice, with small samples it is difficult to assess whether the population distribution is normal or not. You should, however, draw a line plot or histogram of the differences between your pairs of measurements. If their distribution appears to be very skewed, do not use this test.

4.7   Analysis of variance

When to use

1   When testing for differences in the **means** of **more than two populations,** especially when the samples from these populations have been subjected simultaneously to more than one kind of treatment.

2   Provided that several assumptions about your measurements are satisfied. These are discussed in the references mentioned below.

Rationale

Each of the significance tests described in the earlier Sections of this Chapter is suitable only for situations where you wish to compare two samples. As many biological research projects require no more than this, these techniques are very useful. However, one is often faced with more complicated situations than simple comparisons between two samples, and more elaborate statistical techniques are needed. For example, you might wish to test whether three or more samples came from populations with the same mean (or median): for instance whether the mean heights of plants (of a given species) were the same in samples collected from three sites that differed in their soil

pH. In addition, biologists often wish to investigate the effect of two or more factors simultaneously. For instance, you might wish to discover not only the effect of soil pH on plant height, but also the effects of different intensities of illumination and of different exposure to prevailing winds, as well as the combined effect of these factors.

There is a very flexible and useful statistical technique called the analysis of variance (often abbreviated to ANOVA) that is suitable for such problems as these. The principle is quite simple, although the detailed way in which the technique is applied to each particular situation can be complicated. The principle is as follows. Suppose you have several samples of, say, plant height, and that each sample has been subjected experimentally to combinations of treatments to give different soil pH values, different intensities of illumination and different exposures to wind. The heights of the plants in the samples will, of course, vary: some of this variation will be caused by the treatments that you have applied, while the rest will be caused by other factors which, from your point of view, are a nuisance in that they obscure the effects of the treatments in which you are interested. Maybe some plants are shorter than others because the nutrient content of the soil varies randomly within each site; maybe the plants are more crowded together in one place than another and stunt each other's growth; and so on. In the analysis of variance, you work out how much variation there is in all of the samples taken together. The measure of the variability is the variance (see Section 2.3.3). That is, you calculate the total variance present in your measurements. You then work out what proportion of this variance is due to each of the factors in which you are interested. What proportion is due to variation in soil pH? What to illumination? What to wind exposure? What to the combined effects of pH and illumination? What to the combined effects of illumination and wind exposure? And so on. Each of these proportions forms the basis of a separate test statistic (*F*). Thus when you carry out an analysis of variance, you generate several test statistics: one for each factor or combination of factors in which you are interested. For each *F* that we calculate, we know the sampling distribution of *F* under the null hypothesis, which is that populations of plants grown under different conditions of the relevant factor or combination of factors do not differ in their mean heights. By carrying out a single analysis of variance, therefore, we can carry out a whole series of significance tests, and so assess simultaneously the relative importance of the several factors, acting either singly or in combination, on the measurement in which we are interested.

Although the analysis of variance is extremely useful, our experience has been that most students' ecology research projects have been of a sufficiently simple design not to warrant its use. For this reason we do not describe it in any further detail here. If you feel that your own project merits the use of ANOVA, we advise you to make sure that:

(i)   you or your tutor, and preferably both, are already familiar with the analysis of variance, and that you discuss its use with your tutor before you start your project;

(ii)   you are certain which particular version of ANOVA you should use; there are many different versions, each appropriate to a different situation, and there are other tests (such as the Kruskal-Wallis and Friedman tests) which should be used with small samples from populations which are not normally distributed;

(iii)   you have to hand a good textbook describing the analysis of variance. We recommend:

N. T. J. Bailey (1981) *Statistical Methods in Biology*, 2nd edn, Hodder and Stoughton.

R. E. Parker (1979) *Introductory Statistics for Biology*, 2nd edn, Edward Arnold.

4.8   The χ^2 test for association

When to use

1   When you wish to test for an association between **two or more** sets of measurements, each at the **categorical** level.

2   Provided that each measurement is **independent** of the others.

3   Provided that the expected **frequencies,** under the null hypothesis of no association, are **larger than five.**

Rationale

Many of the features of animal and plant life that interest biologists are measured at the categorical level. A biologist might wish to discover, for example, whether the colour of hydrangea flowers depends upon soil pH. Hydrangea flowers are either pink or blue, so when you come across an individual (in flower!) you can classify it as either one or the other. Suppose that you were to investigate the flower colour of hydrangeas in two localities, one chalky, one sandy. Say you examined 60 bushes in the chalky area and found that 20 were pink and 40 blue, whereas of 90 bushes from the sandy area 70 were pink and 20 blue.

You can arrange these numbers in a Table called a **Contingency Table,** as in Table 19(a). Just looking at these

Table 19(a)   Numbers of pink and blue hydrangea bushes observed at two sites, one chalky and one sandy.

	flower colour		
soil type	pink	blue	total
chalky	20	40	60
sandy	70	20	90
total:	90	60	150

Table 19(b)   Numbers of pink and blue hydrangea bushes *observed* at a chalky and a sandy site, as in Table 19(a). The numbers *expected* under a null hypothesis of no association between flower colour and soil type are shown in parentheses.

	flower colour		
soil type	pink	blue	total
chalky	20 (36)	40 (24)	60
sandy	70 (54)	20 (36)	90
total:	90	60	150

numbers suggests that there is a predominance of blue hydrangeas from the chalky area and of pink ones from the sandy area. Can we test this suggestion statistically? Put slightly more formally, can we find out whether there is an **association** between soil type and flower colour? The χ^2 test—pronounced kai (to rhyme with sky) squared where χ is the Greek letter chi—can be used for this purpose. First, you must set up a null hypothesis H_0 which proposes that there is *no* association between soil type and flower colour. The alternative hypothesis H_1 is that there is such an association.

In the present example, a total of 150 bushes were looked at. The next step is to work out how many of these would be expected to be blue and how many pink *if the null hypothesis were true*. We describe below how to calculate these 'expected figures', as they are called, but ask you to accept for the moment that these are the numbers given in parentheses in Table 19(b). If you compare each expected figure with the actual figure next to it (usually referred to as the 'observed figure'), you will see that they are quite a long way apart.

Imagine, now, that the numbers of pink and blue hydrangeas counted in two other areas turned out to be as in Table 20 rather than as in Table 19. Casual inspection of

Table 20 Numbers of pink and blue hydrangea bushes *observed* at two further sites, one chalky and one sandy. Again, the numbers *expected* under the null hypothesis are shown in parentheses.

soil type	flower colour		
	pink	blue	total
chalky	38 (40)	42 (40)	80
sandy	47 (45)	43 (45)	90
total:	85	85	170

Table 20 suggests that here there is little association of flower colour with soil type. We have again calculated the number of bushes of different flower colours that would be expected if the null hypothesis were true. Here these expected figures are much closer to the observed figures than in Table 19.

Comparing Tables 19(b) and 20, it seems that a large discrepancy between observed and expected figures is unlikely if the null hypothesis is true, whereas a small discrepancy is much more likely. We need, therefore, a method of saying just how big this discrepancy is. You might suggest that it would be a good idea to subtract each expected value from its observed value (or vice versa), and add up all of the differences that result. Unfortunately, the result is always zero. (Check this for yourself, for Tables 19(b) and 20.)

To overcome the problem that some differences are positive and others negative, we square them, from Table 20, for example.

observed minus expected $(O - E)$	(observed minus expected)^2 $(O - E)^2$
-2	4
$+2$	4
-2	4
$+2$	4
total: 0	16

One further refinement is needed. A difference of 100 between an observed number (O) and an expected number (E) would seem to be much more extreme when the observed and expected values are, say, 105 and 5 than when they are 1100 and 1000; so you need to put each difference into perspective, as it were. This is achieved by dividing each (observed minus expected)^2 value by the expected value in symbols, $(O - E)^2/E$

(observed minus expected)^2 $(O - E)^2$	(observed minus expected)^2/expected $(O - E)^2/E$
4	$4/40 = 0{\cdot}1$
4	$4/40 = 0{\cdot}1$
4	$4/45 = 0{\cdot}0888889$
4	$4/45 = 0{\cdot}0888889$
	total: $0{\cdot}3777778$

If you add each of the $(O - E)^2/E$ values together, you end up with a single number that indicates the overall discrepancy between the observed and expected figures: the bigger this number, the bigger the discrepancy. This number is called χ^2. Thus:

$$\chi^2 = \sum \frac{(O - E)^2}{E}$$

χ^2 is a test statistic whose sampling distribution under the null hypothesis is known. Although the examples here involve Contingency Tables with only two rows and columns, larger Tables can be treated in exactly the same way. The sampling distribution in fact differs with the numbers of rows and columns in the Contingency Table. To find the correct sampling distribution you calculate the **degrees of freedom,** using the rule:

degrees of freedom = (number of rows in the Contingency Table minus 1) multiplied by (number of columns in the Contingency Table minus 1).

In the present example,

degrees of freedom = $(2 - 1) \times (2 - 1) = 1$

There are Statistical Tables that give critical values of χ^2 for different degrees of freedom and for various significance levels (e.g. Table III(5) in Appendix III). You reject the null hypothesis in favour of the alternative hypothesis if your test statistic is greater than the critical value for the appropriate number of degrees of freedom at your chosen significance level.

There remains the problem of how to calculate expected values (E). Refer back to Table 19(a). Notice that of the 150 bushes examined, 90 were pink and 60 blue. If the null hypothesis is true, we should expect pink and blue bushes in the ratio of 90 : 60 in both the chalky and sandy areas. Now 60 bushes were examined in the chalky area, so we have to find out how many of these should be pink and how many blue, to give a 90 : 60 ratio. The answer is 90/150 of 60 should be pink and 60/150 of 60 should be blue; that is, 36 should be pink and 24 blue—as given in parentheses in the first row of Table 19(b). Similarly, 90 bushes were examined in the sandy area, and again we have to find out how many of these should be pink and how many blue to give a 90 : 60 ratio. The answer is, 90/150 of 90 should be pink and 60/150 of 90 should be blue; that is, 54 should be pink and 36 should be blue—as given in parentheses in the second row of Table 19(b). To calculate expected values for observations in Contingency Tables with more than one row, therefore, the procedure is:

1   Identify the total for the column in which the first observed value lies.

2   Divide this by the grand total (i.e. the number at the foot of the right-hand column in Tables 19 and 20).

3   Multiply the result by the total for the row in which the observed value lies. This gives the expected value for this position in the Table. (*Note:* You will often find that the expected value is *not* a whole number. This is a consequence of the arithmetical procedure that you have to perform, and is not a cause for alarm.)

4   Repeat, to obtain the full set of expected values.

5   Check your answers: expected values along a row should add up to the row total, and expected values down a column should add up to the column total.

This procedure can be used on any size of Contingency Table.

Summary

O = the observed number of items (in any one position in a Contingency Table)

E = the expected number for that position, under the null hypothesis (where E is calculated as 'column total divided by grand total multiplied by row total').

$$\chi^2 = \Sigma \frac{(O-E)^2}{E}, \text{ where you sum } \frac{(O-E)^2}{E}$$

over all positions in the Contingency Table.

If there are a columns and b rows in a Contingency Table, then there are $(a-1) \times (b-1)$ degrees of freedom.

Compare the calculated value of χ^2 with the critical value for $(a-1) \times (b-1)$ degrees of freedom and the appropriate significance level, as given in Table III(5) and *reject* the null hypothesis if

$\chi^2 >$ critical value.

WORKED EXAMPLE

Procedure

1   A common use of the χ^2 test in ecology is to discover whether two (or more) species are distributed independently of one another, or whether, conversely, there is an association between the distribution of one and the other.

Calculation

In this example, we are to investigate whether two plant species, A and B, grow independently of one another or not.

Assume that we have sampled, say, a meadow using quadrats of a given area. As discussed in Section 3.2.7(b), each quadrat can then be classified according to the presence or absence of one or both species:

(a)   both A and B present;

(b)   A present, B absent;

(c)   A absent, B present;

(d)   both A and B absent.

These four categories are arranged in a Contingency Table.

Set up a Contingency Table (see Section 3.2.7b) in which you clearly identify each of the mutually exclusive categories into which you are going to classify your results.

		species A	
		present	absent
species B:	present	(a)	(b)
	absent	(c)	(d)

2   Count how many instances of each category you observe in your sample.

Suppose that 225 quadrats were taken overall in the meadow, and that the results were:

		species A present	species A absent	row total
species B	present	92	58	150
	absent	41	34	75
	total:	133	92	225

3   Calculate row totals and column totals for these observed frequencies (O).

sum of row totals: $150 + 75 = 225$

4   Check that the sum of the column totals equals the sum of the row totals. If not, re-do your calculations.

sum of column totals: $133 + 92 = 225$

5   Calculate the expected frequencies (E) for each position in the Table under the null hypothesis of no association, using the rule '(column total divided by grand total) multiplied by (row total)'

species B	species A present	species A absent	row total
present	$\dfrac{133}{225} \times 150 = 88\cdot6667$	$\dfrac{92}{225} \times 150 = 61\cdot3333$	150
absent	$\dfrac{133}{225} \times 75 = 44\cdot3333$	$\dfrac{92}{225} \times 75 = 30\cdot6667$	75
total:	$133\cdot0000$	$92\cdot0000$	225

6   Check that the expected frequencies add up to the correct (observed) row and column totals, as in step 3. If not, re-do your calculations.

1st row:	$88\cdot6667 + 61\cdot3333 = 150$
2nd row:	$44\cdot3333 + 30\cdot6667 = 75$
1st column:	$88\cdot6667 + 44\cdot3333 = 133$
2nd column:	$61\cdot3333 + 30\cdot6667 = 92$

7   For each position, calculate
$$\frac{(O - E)^2}{E}$$

(a) $\dfrac{(92-88\cdot6667)^2}{88\cdot6667} = 0\cdot125311$

(b) $\dfrac{(58-61\cdot3333)^2}{61\cdot3333} = 0\cdot181156$

(c) $\dfrac{(41-44\cdot3333)^2}{44\cdot3333} = 0\cdot250622$

(d) $\dfrac{(34-30\cdot6667)^2}{30\cdot6667} = 0\cdot362311$

8   Add together all of the figures that you calculated in step 7. This is your test statistic, χ^2, where
$$\chi^2 = \Sigma \frac{(O - E)^2}{E}$$

total: $0\cdot919400$

$\chi^2 = 0\cdot919400$

$= 0\cdot919$ (to three decimal places)

9   Calculate the degrees of freedom using the rule '(number of columns minus one) multiplied by (number of rows minus one)', i.e.

$$(a - 1)(b - 1)$$

degrees of freedom $= (2 - 1) \times (2 - 1)$
$= 1$

10   Compare your test statistic with the critical value given in Table III(5) of Appendix III, for the appropriate degrees of freedom and significance level. If your test statistic is larger than the critical value, reject the null hypothesis and accept the alternative hypothesis.

From Table III(5), the critical value of χ^2 for 1 degree of freedom and a 5% significance level is 3·841. The calculated value is smaller than this. So we cannot reject the null hypothesis, and we accept that there is no association between the distributions of species A and B.

Do's and Don't's for χ^2 tests for association

1   Make sure that you work with sufficiently large numbers. A generally accepted rule of thumb is that none of the expected values under the null hypothesis should be less than five. If you have a large Contingency Table with several rows and columns, and it turns out that some of your expected values *are* smaller than five, you may be able to overcome this problem by combining some of your rows or columns; that is, by lumping together some of your categories. You should only do this if you think it makes biological sense to do so.

2   Make sure that each item that you classify is independent of every other one. For example, in the case of hydrangea flower colour we noted the colour of flowers in each bush. We assumed, possibly not entirely justifiably, that the flower colour of one bush in a locality was independent of the flower colour of another bush. What we were careful to avoid doing was to classify each *flower* on a bush separately as pink or blue, since clearly, the colour of the flowers on the bush are not independent of one another. Similarly, in the worked example on plant associations, we assumed that the category into which you put any one quadrat was independent of the category into which you put any of the others. The important point is to ensure that any one item that you sample is not in a position to influence the measurements you take from any other items in the sample.

3   Make sure that you only use the χ^2 test for associations when you are dealing with categorical variables. That is, you must be able to say to yourself for each item in your samples 'Into which category do I put this?', and having done that, you add one to the frequency of items in the category that you have identified. The calculations must then be carried out using the frequencies themselves. A common error is to calculate a table of percentages from the frequencies, and then to apply the test to the percentages.

4   It is possible to use other versions of the χ^2 test in certain situations which do not lead to a contingency table in the way described. But there is a situation you should be very cautious about. Suppose, for example, you were to collect insects of a given species from one quadrat in each of three sites, in an attempt to see if there is a difference in abundance of the species between the sites. Your results might be as follows:

	Site		
	1	2	3
no. of insects	37	100	15

The data are in a table very like a contingency table, except that is has only one row. It would be possible to use a version of the χ^2 test to investigate the null hypothesis that the abundance of the species is the same at each site (though the details are not the same as for the χ^2 test for association). With the data given above, this null hypothesis would be rejected. However, this does not actually tell you anything very useful. It might have occurred because there really is a difference in the abundance of this insect between the three sites. But it might instead have occurred because the insects within each site do not fly round independently of each other, but instead tend to cluster together. With many species of insect, such clustering is very likely. Maybe there is no overall difference in abundance between the sites, but by chance the quadrat in site 2 happened to include a cluster of insects.

The problem here arises in the *design* of the study rather than in the statistical analysis of the data. If you really wished to discover whether there was a difference in abundance of this insect between site 1 and site 2, for instance, you would have to take several quadrats from each area, count the number of insects in each quadrat, and hence obtain several measurements from each area. You could then treat these counts as samples of measurements at an interval level, and carry out an appropriate significance test, such as a Mann-Whitney U test or a t test.

Often, if an ecological study leads to data in the form of a table of counts with only one row, there will be similar problems in interpreting the results, because the design of the study is inadequate. For this reason we do not describe how to analyse such data here. If your study is going to provide data of this sort, we advise you to discuss the design of the study with your tutor *before* you go ahead with data collection.

4.9 The Spearman rank correlation coefficient

When to use

1 When you wish to discover whether there is an **association** between two sets of measurements that are at the **ordinal** or **interval** level.

2 When you have samples containing **from 7 to 30 pairs** of measurements.

3 When these measurements are reasonably **scattered,** and do not have a U-shaped or inverted U-shaped relationship with one another.

Rationale

It often happens in biological research that you collect two sets of measurements from a sample (i.e. a pair of measurements from each member of the sample) and that you wish to discover how strongly these two sets of measurements are associated with one another. Section 1.1 gives examples, such as whether the numbers of *Gammarus* from different streams vary with the concentration of nitrate nitrogen. There are a number of statistical techniques, known as **correlation** techniques, whose function is to assess the strength of such an association. Each of these techniques ends up by calculating a single number, called a **correlation coefficient,** which indicates the strength of the association. The coefficient lies within the range of $+1$ to -1.

A coefficient of $+1$ indicates a perfect positive correlation between the two sets of measurements. For the Spearman rank correlation coefficient, described here, this means the following: if you were to plot a scatter diagram of your two

sets of measurements, they would either be in a straight line, rising from low values for both sets of measurements on the left of the diagram to high values for both on the right, or, an *increase* in the value of one set of measurements would always be accompanied by an *increase* in value in the other. Figure 42(a) shows three examples of perfect positive correlations. Notice that it does not matter how steeply the line rises or how curved it is: the correlation is perfect so long as both sets of measurements increase together.

A Spearman rank correlation coefficient of -1 indicates a perfect negative correlation. The higher one of the measurements is, the lower is the other measurement of the pair. Again, if you plot a scatter diagram, all the points either lie on a straight line—but this time with the line running from top left to bottom right—or show that an *increase* in one set of measurements is always accompanied by a *decrease* in the other. Again, it is not how steeply the line slopes that is important, but the fact that one set of measurements increases while the other decreases (Figure 42b).

It is very rare, in biological research, to find perfect correlations. Therefore correlation coefficients are seldom as strongly positive as $+1$ or as strongly negative as -1. There are several reasons for this:

1 There may be no association between the two sets of measurements, so that the correlation coefficient is zero. Figure 43a shows such a situation. Here, both soil salinity and the height of a species of plant found growing in the soil vary considerably, but the variation in the two sets of measurements is independent; hence the points in the scatter diagram are dotted around without any clear pattern.

2 There may be an association, but it is obscured by the random variation that is commonly found in biological measurements. Figure 43b shows a situation where there is a positive correlation between rabbit body weight and the quality of the pasture on which the rabbits feed, but that the points are scattered about a straight line rather than lying directly on it. Possibly the rabbit indicated by the circled point, which lies above the line, was unusually heavy because she was pregnant, whereas the rabbit indicated by the point enclosed by a square was unusually light because of disease. The correlation coefficient in this example turns out to be $+0.65$.

3 There may be an association, that is not a simple one. If you were to plot a scattgram of plant abundance against water content of the soil, you might get a picture similar to Figure 43c. The plant in question does not flourish in very dry or very wet soil, and its numbers are highest at intermediate levels of water content. There *is* a relationship between plant numbers and soil water content here, but the

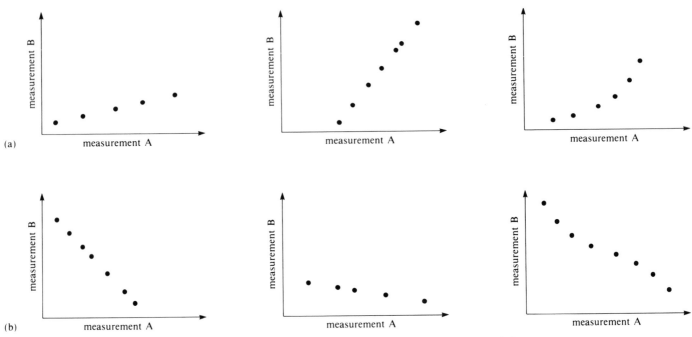

Figure 42.   Examples of perfect (a) positive and (b) negative rank correlations.

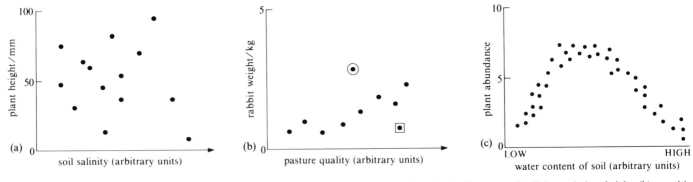

Figure 43.   Three hypothetical examples illustrate correlation problems: (a) the absence of correlation between soil salinity and plant height; (b) a positive correlation between pasture quality and rabbit weight is partially obscured by random variation; (c) a relationship between water content and plant abundance in the shape of an inverted U.

relationship is neither a simple straight line nor a simple curve which steadily rises or steadily falls. Rather, it is a curve of a shape often called an 'inverted U'. Commonly-used correlation techniques will not detect a relationship if the curve is either U-shaped or an inverted U, because the coefficients produced turn out close to zero.

4   There may be an association, but all your measurements are so highly clustered together that a correlation analysis will not reveal the association. For example, there might be a strong association between plant height and the temperature at which the plants were grown which would be perfectly clear if the plants were grown over a wide enough range of temperatures (see Figure 44a). However, if the plants were grown over a narrow temperature range, the association might be difficult to detect (see Figure 44b).

To discover which of situations 1 to 4 applies, it is important to draw a scattgram of your results in order to see what they look like. Only if they are not in the shape of

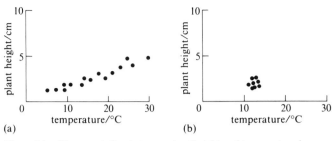

(a) (b)

Figure 44. The association between plant height and temperature is much clearer when the measurements are taken over a wide range (a) than a narrow range (b) of temperature.

a U or an inverted U should you go ahead and calculate a correlation coefficient.

In the Spearman rank correlation coefficient, described here, you arrange your two sets of measurements in two columns, side by side (columns 2 and 4: Table 21). Work out the ranks of the measurements in each of these columns, entering the results in columns 3 and 5 respectively. Suppose, for example, that you wished to discover the extent to which the maximum lengths and weights of chestnut seeds are correlated; the two sets of measurements might appear as in Table 21.

Table 21 The maximum lengths and weights of five chestnut seeds.

(1) seed no.	(2) length/mm	(3) rank of length	(4) weight/g	(5) rank of weight
1	20·5	3	19·3	2
2	23·2	4	22·0	4
3	18·3	1	21·6	3
4	25·3	5	23·8	5
5	19·7	2	18·9	1

Looking first at the lengths, seed number 3 has the smallest length, and so is ranked number 1, seed number 5 has the second smallest, and is ranked number 2, and so on. Ranking the seed weights, seed number 5 is the lightest, and so is ranked number 1; seed number 1 is the second lightest; and so on. Next, you calculate the difference in ranks for each pair of measurements, by subtracting each rank of weight from the corresponding rank of length. The results are listed in Example 1.

If there were a perfect positive correlation between the two measurements, then the seed which ranked 1 for length would rank 1 for weight, the seed which ranked 2 for length

Example 1 Ranks of the lengths and weights in Table 21

seed no.	rank of length	rank of weight	difference
1	3	2	1
2	4	4	0
3	1	3	−2
4	5	5	0
5	2	1	1
		total	0

would rank 2 for weight, and so on. The differences in ranks would, as a result, all be zero, as in Example 2.

Example 2 Positive correlation of ranks

seed no.	rank of length	rank of weight	difference
1	2	2	0
2	5	5	0
3	1	1	0
4	4	4	0
5	3	3	0
		total	0

If, by contrast, there was a perfect negative correlation, then the seed that ranked 1 for length would rank 5 for weight, the seed that ranked 2 for length would rank 4 for weight, and so on, as in Example 3. The differences in ranks would be large: in fact they would be as large as it was possible to achieve for that particular sample size.

Example 3 Negative correlation of ranks

seed no.	rank of length	rank of weight	difference
1	3	3	0
2	1	5	−4
3	4	2	2
4	5	1	4
5	2	4	−2
		total	0

Notice that although in this last example the differences in ranks are bigger than in both of the previous two examples, the summed differences are all zero. This is no accident: if they did not add up to zero you would have ranked them incorrectly. Nonetheless, because the **magnitude** of the differences varies with the degree of association between the

Table 22 Squaring the differences (ΣD^2).

seed no.	Example 1		Example 2		Example 3	
	difference	difference squared	difference	difference squared	difference	difference squared
1	1	1	0	0	0	0
2	0	0	0	0	-4	16
3	-2	4	0	0	2	4
4	0	0	0	0	4	16
5	1	1	0	0	-2	4
total	0	6	0	0	0	40

two sets of measurements, this suggests that if we could concentrate on this magnitude, eliminating the minus signs in some way, we would have a measure of association. This is achieved by squaring each difference (Table 22).

The totals of the squared differences now reflect (in some way) the degree of association between the two sets of measurements. Where there is a perfect positive correlation, the total is zero, where there is a weak positive correlation the total is 6, and where there is a strong negative correlation, the total is 40.

For brevity, we can denote the sum of the squared differences by the symbol ΣD^2. ΣD^2 is not itself a correlation coefficient: in the three examples here it varies from 0 to 40, rather than from $+1$ to -1.

Suppose we now ask the question 'How big is ΣD^2 in relation to the maximum value (ΣD^2_{max}) it could take?' In Example 1, ΣD^2 is 6, and we know that the maximum possible value of ΣD^2 is 40, so ΣD^2 is $6/40 = 0\cdot15$ times the maximum value, ΣD^2_{max}. In Example 2, ΣD^2 is 0, which is $0/40 = 0$ times the maximum value. In Example 3, ΣD^2 is 40, which is $40/40 = 1$ times the maximum possible value. This is set out in Table 23.

This ratio, $\Sigma D^2/\Sigma D^2_{max}$, looks more promising as a correlation coefficient: at least the numbers are in the range of 0 to 1, instead of 0 to 40 as in Table 22. But we are not quite there yet, because for a perfect positive correlation the value of $\Sigma D^2/\Sigma D^2_{max}$ is 0, rather than the 1 that we require.

To turn $\Sigma D^2/\Sigma D^2_{max}$ into a number with the required properties, you multiply it by two and subtract the result from 1:

$$\text{correlation coefficient} = 1 - 2(\Sigma D^2/\Sigma D^2_{max})$$

Table 24 shows what happens in the three examples. It can be seen that this manipulation produces numbers that range from $+1$ where there is a perfect positive correlation to -1 where there is a perfect negative correlation. There is one further step to simplify the calculations, and this is to do with the calculation of ΣD^2_{max}. It would be tedious to work out the maximum possible value for ΣD^2 for every sample size by calculating this value when the two sets of measurements are perfectly negatively correlated (as

Table 23 Values for $\Sigma D^2/\Sigma D^2_{max}$.

	Example		
	1	2	3
ΣD^2	6	0	40
ΣD^2_{max}	40	40	40
$\dfrac{\Sigma D^2}{\Sigma D^2_{max}}$	$\dfrac{6}{40} = 0\cdot15$	$\dfrac{0}{40} = 0$	$\dfrac{40}{40} = 1$

Table 24 Developing a correlation coefficient (from $\Sigma D/\Sigma D^2_{max}$).

	Example		
	1	2	3
$\dfrac{\Sigma D^2}{\Sigma D^2_{max}}$	$0\cdot15$	0	1
$1 - \dfrac{2\Sigma D^2}{\Sigma D^2_{max}}$	$1-(2\times0\cdot15)$ $=0\cdot7$	$1-(2\times0)$ $=1$	$1-(2\times1)$ $=-1$

in Example 3). Fortunately it is possible to show mathematically that

$$\Sigma D^2_{max} = n(n^2 - 1)/3$$

where n is the sample size. (If you do not believe this, try it out for yourself on a few sample sizes.) Substituting for ΣD^2_{max} in the equation:—

$$\text{correlation coefficient} \quad = 1 - \frac{2\Sigma D^2}{\Sigma D^2_{max}}$$

this gives what is known as the Spearman rank correlation coefficient, r_s:

$$r_s = 1 - \frac{6\Sigma D^2}{n(n^2 - 1)}$$

Usually in biological research, one is not so much interested in the precise value of r_s as in whether (or not) r_s is close to zero. If r_s *is* close to zero, you accept the null hypothesis that there is no correlation between the two features under investigation. If, by contrast, r_s is sufficiently far from zero, then you reject the null hypothesis, and accept the alternative hypothesis that there is a correlation between the two features—positive or negative according to whether r_s is positive or negative. The coefficient r_s can therefore be used as a test statistic in a significance test. The sampling distribution of r_s under a null hypothesis of no correlation is known, and Table III(6) in Appendix III shows critical values for r_s for different sample sizes and different levels of significance. You reject the null hypothesis in favour of the alternative hypothesis at the appropriate level of significance if the calculated value of r_s is greater than or equal to the critical value given in the Table.

To illustrate the use of the Table, suppose that your sample size is 18 and that your calculated value of r_s is $0 \cdot 522$.

Reading along the row for sample sizes of 18 until you come to the column for a 5% significance level, the critical value for r_s turns out to be $0 \cdot 475$. For a 2% level of significance the critical value is $0 \cdot 564$. The calculated value of r_s lies between these two values, and so one can reject the null hypothesis in favour of the alternative hypothesis at the 5% level but not at the 2% level of significance.

Summary

D	= the difference in rank between a pair of measurements,
ΣD^2	= the sum of the squares of all such differences.
n	= the sample size: that is, the number of pairs of measurements.
r_S	= Spearman's rank correlation coefficient

$$= 1 - \frac{6\Sigma D^2}{n(n^2 - 1)}$$

WORKED EXAMPLE

Procedure

1   Arrange your two sets of measurements side by side in two columns, so that the two measurements from a given pair lie on the same row.

Calculation

seed no.	length/mm	weight/g
1	20·5	19·3
2	23·2	22·0
3	18·3	21·6
4	25·3	23·8
5	19·7	18·9
6	25·3	24·7
7	15·6	18·2
8	20·8	19·5

(The first five measurements are the same as for the chestnut seeds discussed earlier, Table 21, three more have been added.)

2   Draw a scatter diagram of one set of measurements against the other. (Figure 45).

If the points appear to lie on a U-shaped or inverted U-shaped curve (Figure 43c) or if they are all squashed together (Figure 44a) do not proceed with the correlation test: simply describe the apparent relationship between the two sets of measurements verbally. Otherwise, proceed to step 3.

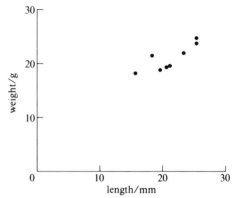

Figure 45.   The relationship between weight and length of chestnut seeds from the table above.

3   Rank each measurement in column 2. Give the smallest measurement rank 1, the next smallest rank 2, and so on, and enter them in column 3. If some of the measurements have the same value give them the average of their ranks (for example, seeds 4 and 6 are both 25·3 mm long and would occupy ranks 7 and 8 if they were not quite identical, so give them both the average of these ranks of 7.5).

Do the same for the measurements in column 4, entering the ranks in column 5.

(1) seed no.	(2) length/mm	(3) rank of length	(4) weight/g	(5) rank of weight
1	20·5	4	19·3	3
2	23·2	6	22·0	6
3	18·3	2	21·6	5
4	25·3	7·5	23·8	7
5	19·7	3	18·9	2
6	25·3	7·5	24·7	8
7	15·6	1	18·2	1
8	20·8	5	19·5	4

4   Subtract each rank in column 5 from the corresponding rank in column 3.

(1) seed no	(3) rank of length	(5) rank of weight	difference in ranks (length minus weight)
1	4	3	1
2	6	6	0
3	2	5	−3
4	7·5	7	0·5
5	3	2	1
6	7·5	8	−0·5
7	1	1	0
8	5	4	1
			total 0

5   Add up the differences; if the total is not zero, check your calculations, since you have made a mistake.

6   Square each of the differences.

seed no.	difference in ranks	difference squared
1	1	1
2	0	0
3	−3	9
4	0·5	0·25
5	1	1
6	−0·5	0·25
7	0	0
8	1	1
	total (ΣD^2)	12·5

7   Add up the squared differences. The total is ΣD^2.

8   Work out the sample size, n (the number of pairs of measurements).

$$n = 8$$

9   Work out $n(n^2 - 1)$

$$8(8^2 - 1) = 8 \times 63 = 504$$

10   Multiply ΣD^2 by 6 and divide by $n(n^2 - 1)$.

$$\frac{12 \cdot 5 \times 6}{504} = 0 \cdot 14881$$

11   Subtract the result from 1 to find r_s;

$$r_s = 1 - \frac{6\Sigma D^2}{n(n^2 - 1)}$$

$$r_s = 1 - 0 \cdot 14881$$
$$= 0 \cdot 85119$$
$$= 0 \cdot 851 \text{ (to three decimal places)}$$

12   Compare r_s with the critical values in Table III(6) of Appendix III for a test with a sample size of n.

Critical value for r_s with $n = 8$ is 0·833 at the 2% significance level and 0·881 at the 1% significance level.

The calculated value of r_s lies between these two values, so we reject the null hypothesis of no correlation between weight and maximum length at the 2% (but not at the 1%) level of significance.

Do's and Don't's for the Spearman rank correlation coefficient

1   Avoid working with sample sizes of less than 7 or 8, since random variation is more likely to obscure a genuine association with very small samples. With large samples the procedure of working out the ranks becomes very tedious, and so it is best to avoid samples of more than 30.

2   Do not use the Spearman rank correlation coefficient if (i) the relationship between the two sets of variables appears to be U-shaped, or (ii) if the amount of variation in one or both sets of measurements is very small.

3   Be careful how you interpret the results of your analysis. If you show that a correlation exists, this does not explain *why* it exists. For instance, in our example of chestnut seed weights and lengths, the measurements show a significant positive correlation. Say a similar correlation had been found between body weight and wing span for moths. There could be three potential explanations for this: (i) big bodies are responsible for the growth of big wings; (ii) big wings are responsible for the growth of big bodies; (iii) some other factor promotes both big wings and big bodies, and body weights and wing spans do not have any direct effect on each other.

But correlation does not imply causation. There may be no biological explanation for the correlation in terms of cause and effect.

Use of a correlation coefficient cannot tell us which of these three alternatives is correct, and you would have to carry out further investigations to find the answer. Remember, therefore, that there are in general four possible explanations for any correlation that you reveal.

Explanation 1:   A causes B;

Explanation 2:   B causes A;

Explanation 3:   A and B independently depend upon C.

Explanation 4:   Coincidence

4.10   Linear regression

When to use

1   When you have two sets of measurements at the **interval** level, which are arranged in **pairs**.

2   When you wish to use the measurements in **one set** to **predict** values in **the other**.

3   Provided that any underlying relationship between the two sets of variables is **linear**, that both sets of measurements are reasonably **scattered**, and that the **residuals** (see below) do not vary with the size of the measurements belonging to the set from which the predictions are to be made.

Rationale

Before reading further, make sure you understand the Section on correlation, Section 4.9.

Linear regression is similar to correlation, in that both deal with two sets of measurements, and both are concerned with the association between them. There is, however, an important difference. When you calculate a correlation coefficient, you are interested in discovering *how strong* the association is, and this strength is indicated by the size of the correlation coefficient. In regression analysis, by contrast, you are interested in *predicting* the values of measurements in one of your sets, from values of measurements in the other set. In Section 4.9, the worked example on chestnut seed weight and length showed that the Spearman rank correlation coefficient r_s was 0.851, indicating a strong association between the two features. Linear regression applied to the same measurements would help us to answer the question 'If I have a seed of length x mm, what is the weight likely to be?' or the converse, 'If I have a seed of weight y g, what is its length likely to be?'

To take a different example, you might wish to know how temperature affects plant growth. You might conduct experiments on three different species, growing several individuals of each plant under a variety of different temperature regimes for a given length of time. Suppose, for the moment, that you obtained the unlikely result that in each case there was a perfect positive correlation between temperature and plant growth, so that when you plotted the increases in plant height against temperature for each species, you obtained the results shown in Figure 46. In each case, the correlation is perfect and the line joining the points is straight. However, the lines differ one from another. In species 1, there is no growth at all if the temperature is 0 °C, and a higher temperature only slightly increases the growth rate. In species 2, again there is no growth if the temperature is zero, but a higher temperature has a much larger effect on growth. In species 3, by contrast, there is some growth even at 0 °C, but the increase in growth is only slight when the temperature is higher.

If you knew the temperature at which a plant of species 1 was to be grown, you could predict exactly how much it would grow during the course of the experiment, and similarly with a plant from species 2 or species 3. You would simply find the point on the temperature scale for the appropriate species, move vertically upwards from that point until you came to the sloping line, and then read off the point on the vertical scale that you had reached. Note, however, that you have to use a different graph for each species: there is a perfect correlation in each instance, but the nature of the straight line relationship differs in each.

Referring again to Figure 46 you can see that the two features in which the sloping lines differ are:

(i) their slope—for one species it is steep, for the other two it is shallow;

(ii) the point at which they cross the vertical axis—for two species it is at zero, for one it is at 3 cm.

When there is a straight line relationship between two sets of measurements, you can define exactly where the line goes provided you know the slope, and the point at which the line crosses the vertical axis. To measure the slope, you ask the question 'By how many units does the measurement plotted along the vertical axis change for every unit that the measurement plotted along the horizontal axis changes?' If, for example, plant growth increases by 2 cm for every degree Celsius rise in temperature, the slope is 2; if the increase in plant growth is 3 cm per degree, the slope is 3; and so on.

The rule for predicting a measurement on the vertical axis from a measurement on the horizontal axis is therefore as follows: take your horizontal axis measurement, multiply it by the slope, and add to the result the value on the vertical axis at which the sloping line crosses that axis. In symbols:

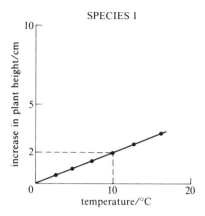

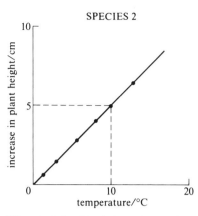

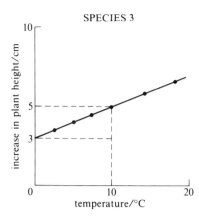

Figure 46. Three different relationships between temperature and plant growth.

Let x = horizontal axis measurement (e.g. temperature);
  y = vertical axis measurement (e.g. increase in plant height);
  m = slope;
  c = point at which sloping line crosses vertical axis.

Then $y = mx + c$

Figure 46 shows the slopes and values of c for the three plant species growing at different temperatures, and illustrates how you can use the equation $y = mx + c$ to predict plant growth from temperature.

There is no reason, in principle, why you should wish to use this prediction in only one direction. You might, for some reason, wish to use your plants as a thermometer, and predict temperature from plant growth. To do so, you would simply plot plant lengths along the horizontal axis, temperatures along the vertical, and proceed exactly as above.

Perfect straight line relationships are very rare in biological research. More usually, points plotted on a graph are scattered to a greater or lesser extent about a line, the scatter being the result of random variation.

When we carry out linear regression, we assume that there really is a straight line relationship between the two features under investigation (which is why the technique is called *linear* regression), and we estimate the position of the best-fit line through the scattered points (see Figure 47). But how do we decide what *is* the best line? Intuitively, it seems that a good line will run close to all of the points, whereas a bad one will be a long way from them. Judged on this criterion, line A in Figure 47 is much better than line B, and C is marginally better than B.

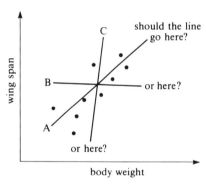

Figure 47. The problem of where best to draw the straight line representing the relationship underlying the two sets of measurements.

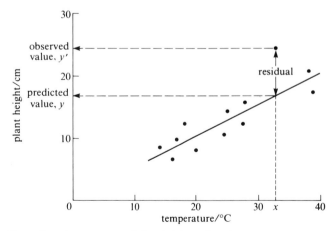

Figure 48. A scattergram of plant height against the temperature at which each individual was grown. The dots depict data points: the diagonal presents a summary of the general relationship between plant height and temperature.

Clearly there needs to be an objective way of measuring how close a given line runs to all of the points in a scattergram. The method used is as follows. Imagine that a scattergram of, say, plant height against temperature looks like Figure 48, and that you draw a straight line through the scattered points. For a given temperature, x, the line predicts that the corresponding plant height will be y. Suppose, however, that a plant that has been grown at temperature x is in reality much taller than predicted—perhaps it has a height of y'. The vertical distance $y' - y$ between that point and the line, shown by the double-headed arrow in Figure 48, tells us how big is the difference between the observed and the predicted heights of that plant. Put differently, the vertical distance tells us how large is the *error* in the prediction made by the line.

The technical term for this error is the **residual**. If you look at all of the points in Figure 48, you will see that some lie above the line and some below: in some the residuals are positive and in others negative. To measure how good a fit the line achieves, it is necessary to take all of these residuals into account. If you were simply to add them all up, the positive residuals would tend to cancel out the negative ones; so to overcome this problem each residual is squared. (When you multiply a negative number by itself, the result is a positive number, and hence squaring the residuals produces a set of positive numbers.) You can then add together all the squared residuals, and this total gives a measure of how well the line fits the points in the scattergram: the smaller the total, the better the fit. The line with the best fit of all is the one that gives the smallest total value for the squared residuals. There is a technique for finding this straight line, often referrred to as the 'least squares' method of regression analysis. It allows you to calculate the slope (m) of the 'best fit' line and the point ($x = 0$, $y = c$) at which it crosses the vertical axis, from the data in the scattergram. That is, the technique enables you to identify the line that gives the smallest sum of squared residuals. The calculations can be time-consuming, and you are advised to use a calculator or computer program if possible. We shall not describe the rationale behind the technique in this Project Guide, but simply summarise how to calculate m and c as follows.

Summary

Let the sample plotted along the horizontal axis be called sample X. Let it have a sample mean of $\bar{x}$, and let any one measurement in the sample be called x.

Let the sample plotted along the vertical axis be called sample Y. Let it have a sample mean of $\bar{y}$, and let any one measurement in the sample be called y. The measurements in the samples must be arranged in their pairs, just as when calculating a correlation coefficient.

The slope of the required straight line is given by

$$m = \frac{\Sigma(x - \bar{x})(y - \bar{y})}{\Sigma(x - \bar{x})^2}$$

The point at which this line crosses the vertical axis is given by

$$c = \bar{y} - m\bar{x}$$

Having calculated m and c, you can draw the straight line with slope m which crosses the vertical axis at point c. You can also predict any particular value of sample Y from any particular value of sample X, by using either the line you have drawn or the equation $y = mx + c$.

WORKED EXAMPLE

Procedure

1   Arrange your two sets of measurements side by side in two columns, so that each pair of measurements lies on the same row. The measurements *from* which you wish to make predictions should go in the second column, the measurements *about* which you wish to make predictions should go in the fourth. (Leave columns 3 and 5 empty for the present.)

Calculation

We shall use the same chestnut seed measurements as for the correlation analysis in the worked example in Section 4.9:

(1) seed no.	(2) length, x/mm	(3)	(4) weight, y/g	(5)
1	20·5		19·3	
2	23·2		22·0	
3	18·3		21·6	
4	25·3		23·8	
5	19·7		18·9	
6	25·3		24·7	
7	15·6		18·2	
8	20·8		19·5	
total	168·7		168·0	

2   Draw a scattergram of your measurements (Figure 49). The measurements *from* which you wish to make predictions should go along the horizontal axis; the measurements *about* which you wish to make predictions should go along the vertical axis. If the points appear to lie on a curve rather than a straight line, or if they all appear to be squashed together, do not proceed with the regression analysis but use another method. (See Do's and Don'ts for more details.)

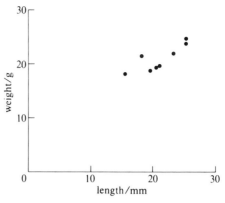

Figure 49.   The relationship between length and weight of chestnut seeds from the table on p. 82.

3   Calculate the mean for columns 2 and 4, then subtract each measurement in these columns from their means, entering the answers in columns 3 and 5 respectively.

Total columns 3 and 5. They should both be zero (or very close to it, since rounding errors may result in slight deviations from zero). If they are not, re-do your calculations.

$$\text{mean length, } \bar{x} = \frac{168\cdot7}{8} \qquad \text{mean weight, } \bar{y} = \frac{168\cdot0}{8}$$

$$= 21\cdot0875 \text{ mm} \qquad\qquad = 21\cdot0 \text{ g}$$

(1) seed no.	(2) length, x/mm	(3) $x - \bar{x}$	(4) weight, y/g	(5) $y - \bar{y}$
1	20·5	−0·5875	19·3	−1·7
2	23·2	2·1125	22·0	1·0
3	18·3	−2·7875	21·6	0·6
4	25·3	4·2125	23·8	2·8
5	19·7	−1·3875	18·9	−2·1
6	25·3	4·2125	24·7	3·7
7	15·6	−5·4875	18·2	−2·8
8	20·8	−0·2875	19·5	−1·5
total	168·7	0·0000	168·0	0·0

4   Multiply each value in column 3 by the corresponding value in column 5. Enter the results in column 6, then total them

	(3) $(x - \bar{x})$	(5) $(y - \bar{y})$	(6) $(x - \bar{x})(y - \bar{y})$
	−0·5875	−1·7	0·99875
	2·1125	1·0	2·1125
	−2·7875	0·6	−1·6725
	4·2125	2·8	11·795
	−1·3875	−2·1	2·91375
	4·2125	3·7	15·5863
	−5·4875	−2·8	15·365
	−0·2875	−1·5	0·43125
total	0·0000	0·0	47·5300

This gives $\Sigma(x - \bar{x})(y - \bar{y})$

$\Sigma(x - \bar{x})(y - \bar{y}) = 47.53$

5 Square each value in column 3. Then add the results together and enter them at the foot of column 7.

(3) $x - \bar{x}$	(7) $(x - \bar{x})^2$
−0·5875	0·34516
2·1125	4·46266
−2·7875	7·77016
4·2125	17·7456
−1·3875	1·92516
4·2125	17·7456
−5·4875	30·1127
−0·2875	0·082656
total	80·18875

This gives $\Sigma(x - \bar{x})^2$

$\Sigma(x - \bar{x})^2 = 80.18875$

6 Divide the number you calculated in step 4 by the number you calculated in step 5. This gives the slope m:

$$m = \frac{\Sigma(x - \bar{x})(y - \bar{y})}{\Sigma(x - \bar{x})^2}$$

$$m = \frac{47.53}{80.18875} = 0.592727$$

7 Multiply the slope m by the sample mean length $\bar{x}$ which you calculated in step 3.

$m \times \bar{x} = 0.592725 \times 21.0875$

$= 12.4991$

8 Subtract this figure from $\bar{y}$, the sample mean weight that you calculated in step 3. This gives the value of c, the point at which the sloping line crosses the vertical axis:

$c = \bar{y} - m\bar{x}$

$c = \bar{y} - m\bar{x}$
$= 21.0 - 12.4991$
$= 8.5009$

9 Write down the equation relating y to x:

$y = mx + c$

$y = 0.59x + 8.5$ (to two significant figures)

10 Draw a straight line through your scattergram with slope m and crossing the vertical axis at c, by the following method:

(i) Mark the value of c on the vertical axis. This gives you your first point on the line, the point $x = 0$, $y = c$. (Figure 50)

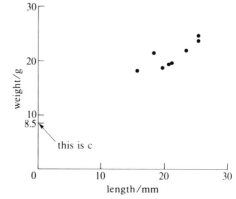

Figure 50

(ii) Work out the value of y corresponding to a convenient large value of x near the right-hand end of the horizontal scale, using the equation

$y = mx + c$

Choose, say, $x = 30$. Then

$y = 0.59 \times 30 + 8.5$

(iii) Enter this second point on the scatter diagram.

$$= 17\!\cdot\!70 + 8\!\cdot\!5$$

$$= 26\!\cdot\!2$$

(iv) Work out another value of y from a value of x somewhere in the middle of the horizontal scale. Enter this third point on the scatter diagram.

(v) Join the three points you have entered with a straight line (Figure 51). (If the three points do not lie on a straight line, check your calculations.) This is called the *regression line of seed weight on seed length*

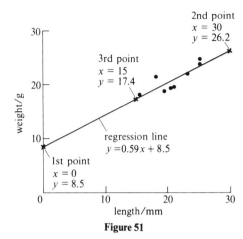

Figure 51

11 Predict the value of y corresponding to any value of x. There are two methods:

(i) use the regression line to predict y

What is the value of y predicted from $x = 25\!\cdot\!0$?

(i)

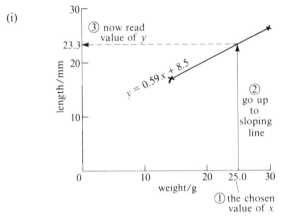

Figure 52

(ii) or use the equation $y = mx + c$ to predict y.

From the regression line, if $x = 25\!\cdot\!0$, then $y = 23\!\cdot\!3$.

(ii) Using the equation, if $x = 25\!\cdot\!0$,

$$y = 0\!\cdot\!59 \times 25\!\cdot\!0 + 8\!\cdot\!5$$

$$= 14\!\cdot\!75 + 8\!\cdot\!5$$

$$= 23\!\cdot\!25$$

Do's and Don't's with Linear Regressions

1 Always plot a scattergram of your measurements before you carry out a regression analysis. The regression technique described here assumes that there *is* a straight line relationship between the two sets of measurements, so check from the scattergram that the relationship, if it exists, is at least not curved. (If you have small samples, it may not be possible to be sure of this.) The technique also makes certain assumptions about the distances that the points lie from the regression line (the 'residuals'). One of these assumptions is that the size of the residuals does not vary

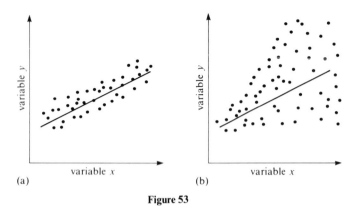

Figure 53

with the size of the measurements along the horizontal axis (see Figure 53a). You should check this visually from your scattergram.

If the residuals at one part of the horizontal scale are clearly different in size from those at other parts of the scale, then do not use regression analysis (Figure 53b).

2   Be very cautious about using your straight line to predict values of x which are a long way from the measurements you have made. For instance, you might think of using the straight line in Figure 51 to predict the weight of a seed 5 mm long ($x = 5$). But there is no evidence from the measurements in the table that a straight line accurately describes the relationship between length and weight for seeds this small. All the seeds on which the straight line is based are between 15 and 26 mm long. The straight line should not, therefore, be used for seeds much less than 15 mm long.

3   There are many elaborations of the basic technique of linear regression. For example you can, if you wish, calculate confidence limits for the values of m (the slope) and c (the value of y when the sloping line crosses the vertical axis). You can, if you wish, do significance tests on whether, for example, your sample could have come from a population with a slope of a particular value, and so on. Consult a statistician if you wish to pursue any of these avenues.

4   Do not carry out regression analysis unless your measurements are at the interval level.

Summary and Objective for Chapter 4

This Chapter presents ten commonly used statistical techniques, plus a decision chart to enable you to identify which technique is best suited to your problem. You should now be able to:

★ use the decision chart and carry out the appropriate techniques on your data.

Appendix I   References

1.   Suggestions for Further Reading on fieldwork techniques in general and useful background texts

BAKER, J. M. and WOLF, W. J. (1987). *Biological surveys of estuaries and coasts.* Cambridge University Press.

BENNETT, D. P. and HUMPHRIES, D. A. (1965). *Introduction to Field Biology.* Edward Arnold.

BURNHAM, C. P. (1980). The Soils of England & Wales. *Field Studies,* **5,** 349–363*.

CROTHERS, J. H. (1981). On the graphical presentation of quantitative data. *Field Studies,* **5,** 487–511*.

ELTON, Charles S. (1966). *The Pattern of Animal Communities.* Methuen.

GREIG-SMITH, P. (1983). *Quantitative Plant Ecology.* Studies in Ecology No. 9. Blackwell.

HAWKSWORTH, D. L. and ROSE, F. (1976). *Lichens as pollution monitors.* Studies in Biology No. 66. Edward Arnold.

HELLAWELL, J. M. (1978). *Biological surveillance of rivers: a biological monitoring handbook* NERC. [available from the Water Research Council, Stevenage Lab., Elder Way, Stevenage, Herts SG1 1TH.]

HYNES, H. B. N. (1960). *The Biology of Polluted Waters.* Liverpool University Press.

HYNES, H. B. N. (1970). *The Ecology of Running Waters.* Liverpool University Press.

KERSHAW, K. A. (1984). *Quantitative and Dynamic Ecology.* 3rd Edition. Arnold.

MABEY, R. (1974). *The Pollution Handbook.* The Advisory Centre for Education/Sunday Times Clean Air and Water Surveys. Penguin.

NICHOLS, D. (1983). *Safety in Biological Fieldwork— guidance notes for codes of practice.* 2nd Ed. Institute of Biology, London.

PRICE, J. H., IRVINE, D. E. G. and FARNHAM, W. F. (1980). *The Shore Environment. Vol. 1 Methods: Vol. 2 Ecosystems.* Academic Press. The Systematics Association Special Volume No. 17.

SOUTHWOOD, T. R. E. (1966). *Ecological Methods, with particular reference to the study of insect populations.* Methuen.

TRUDGILL, S. T. (1989). Soil Types: a field identification guide. *Field Studies* **7.**

WILLIS, A. J. (1973). *An Introduction to Plant Ecology.* 2nd Ed. George Allen and Unwin.

2.   Sources of Keys for Identification

KERRICH, G. J., HAWKSWORTH, D. L. and SIMS, R. W. (Eds: 1978). *Key Works to the fauna and flora of the British Isles and Northwestern Europe.* The Systematics Association Special Volume No. 9. Academic Press.

Higher Plants

General

ARNOLD, S. M. (1983). *A Simple Field Key to Common British Wild Flowers.* Lockington Publishing (Available from the author, 14 Main Street, Hotham, York YO4 3UF.)
[A good key for beginners, with a clear glossary.]

CLAPHAM, A. R., TUTIN, T. G. and WARBURG, E. F. (1981). *Excursion Flora of the British Isles.* 3rd Ed. Cambridge University Press.
[This is the definitive key to British vascular plants, using the names from *Flora Europaea,* but it has no illustrations and is difficult for beginners.]

†FITTER, R., FITTER, A. and BLAMEY, M. (1974). *The Wild Flowers of Britain and Northern Europe.* Collins.
[A good book for those not familiar with plant taxonomy.]

HAYWARD, J. (1986). *A New Key to Wild Flowers.* Cambridge University Press
[AIDGAP tested.]

KEBLE MARTIN, W. (1982). *The New Concise British Flora.* Ebury Press and Michael Joseph.

PHILLIPS, R. (1977). *Wild Flowers in Britain.* Pan Books.

†ROSE, F. (1981). *The Wild Flower Key.* Warne.
[A guide which contains keys to species and coloured illustrations. There are also keys to the vegetative characters which enable you to identify plants not in flower.]

†SCHAUER, T. (1982). *A Field Guide to the Wild Flowers of Britain and Europe.* Collins

TUTIN, T. G. *and others* (1964–1980). *Flora Europaea.* Cambridge University Press.
[Not for beginners, this is the definitive flora for Europe in five volumes. It should be available in reference libraries.]

Specific groups of higher plants

BUNCE, R. G. H. (1982). *A Field Key for classifying British Woodland Vegetation.* Part 1 NERC.

†These books are complementary to some extent as each illustrates a slightly different range of species.

CHANCELLOR, R. J. (1966). *Identification of Weed Seedlings of Farm and Garden*. Blackwell.

HASLAM, S., SINKER, C. A. and WOLSELEY, P. (1975; 1982). British Water Plants. *Field Studies*, **4**, 243–351.*

HUBBARD, C. E. (1984). *Grasses*. 3rd Ed. Penguin Books. [Keys to grasses in flower and in the vegetative state.]

JERMY, A. C., CHATER, A. O. and DAVID, R. W. (1982). *Sedges of the British Isles*. Botanical Society of the British Isles (BSBI) Handbook No. 1 (2nd Edition).

LOUSLEY, J. E. and KENT, D. H. (1981). *Docks and Knotweeds*. BSBI Handbook No. 3.

MEIKLE, R. D. (1984). *Willows and Poplars of Great Britain and Ireland*. BSBI Handbook No. 4.

MITCHELL, Alan (1978). *A Field Guide to the Trees of Britain and Northern Europe*. Collins.

PANKHURST, R. J. and ALLINSON, J. E. (1985). British Grasses: a punched card key to grasses in the vegetative state. *Occasional Publications of the Field Studies Council* No. 10*.

PHILLIPS, R. (1980). *Trees in Britain, Europe and North America*. Pan Books.

PHILLIPS, R. (1980). *Grasses, Ferns, Mosses and Lichens of Great Britain and Ireland*. Pan Books.

READER'S DIGEST ASSOCIATION LTD. (1981). *Field Guide to the Trees and Shrubs of Britain*. Reader's Digest.

SINKER, C. A. (1975). A lateral key to Common Grasses. *Bulletin of the Shropshire Conservation Trust*, 34. [Reprinted in two different formats and available from the 'Field Studies'* address or from any FSC Field Centre.]

WIGGINTON, M. J. & GRAHAM, G. G. (1981). *Guide to the Identification of some Difficult Plant Groups*. Nature Conservancy Council: England Field Unit, Occasional Paper No. 1.

Other Plants

BELCHER, Hilary, and SWALE, Erica (1979). *An illustrated guide to River Phytoplankton*. ITE, HMSO.

DICKINSON, Carola I. (1963). *British Seaweeds*. Eyre & Spottiswoode.

HISCOCK, S. (1979). A Field Key to the British Brown Seaweeds (Phaeophyta). *Field Studies*, **5**, 1–44.*

HISCOCK, S. (1986). A Field Key to the British Red Seaweeds. *Occasional Publication of the Field Studies Council* No. 13.*

JAHNS, H. M. (1983). *Collins Guide to Ferns, Mosses and Lichens*. Collins.

LANGE, M. and HORA, F. B. (1963). *Collins Guide to Mushrooms and Toadstools*. Collins.

PAGE, C. N. (1982). *The Ferns of Britain and Ireland*. Cambridge University Press.

PHILLIPS, R. (1980). *Grasses, Ferns, Mosses and Lichens of Great Britain and Ireland*. Pan Books.

PHILLIPS, R. (1981). *Mushrooms and other Fungi of Great Britain and Europe*. Pan Books.

SYKES, J. B. (1981). An illustrated guide to the Diatoms of British Coastal Plankton. *Field Studies*, **5**, 425–468.*

WATSON, E. V. (1981). *British Mosses and Liverworts*. 3rd Ed. Cambridge University Press.

Marine Invertebrates

General

BARRETT, John and OVENDEN, Denys (1981). *Collins Handguide to the Sea Coast*. Collins.

BARRETT, J. H. and YONGE, C. M. (1958). *Collins Pocket Guide to the Seashore*. Collins. [Although written nearly 30 years ago, and therefore inevitably out-of-date in some respects, this book remains the most complete general guide on the market.]

CAMPBELL, A. C. & NICHOLLS, James (1976). *The Hamlyn Guide to the Seashore and Shallow Seas of Britain and Europe*. Hamlyn.

QUIGLEY, M. and CRUMP, R. (1986). *Animals and plants of rocky shores*. Blackwell, Oxford.

READER'S DIGEST ASSOCIATION LTD. (1984). *Field Guide to the Water Life of Britain*. Reader's Digest. [Includes marine, brackish and fresh water: mainly zoological: some sections better than others.]

Coelenterates (Cnidarians)

MANUEL, R. L. (1980). *The Anthozoa of the British Isles*. A colour guide produced for the Underwater Conservation Society by R. Earll. [Obtainable from Dr R. Earll, Zoology Dept, Manchester University, M13 9PL.]

MANUEL, R. L. (1981). *British Anthozoa*. Synopses of the British Fauna (New Series) No. 18. Published for the Linnean Society of London and the Estuarine and Brackish Water Sciences Association by Cambridge University Press.

Worms

BALL, Ian R. and REYNOLDSON, T. B. (1981). *British Planarians*. Synopses of the British Fauna (New Series) No. 19. Published for the Linnean Society of London and the Estuarine and Brackish Water Sciences Association by Cambridge University Press.

GIBSON, Ray (1982). *British Nemerteans*. Synopses of the British Fauna (New Series) No. 24. Published for the Linnean Society of London and the Estuarine and Brackish Water Sciences Association by Cambridge University Press.

PRUDHOE, S. (1982). *British Polyclad Turbellarians*. Synopses of the British Fauna (New Series) No. 26. Published for the Linnean Society of London and the Estuarine and Brackish Water Sciences Association by Cambridge University Press.

Crustaceans

CROTHERS, John and CROTHERS, Marilyn (1983: 1988). A Key to the crabs and crab-like animals of British Inshore Waters. *Field Studies*, **5**, 753–806.*

INGLE, R. W. (1983). *Shallow-water Crabs*. Synopses of the British Fauna (New Series) No. 25. Published for the Linnean Society of London and the Estuarine and Brackish Water Sciences Association by Cambridge University Press.

NAYLOR, R. (1972). *British Marine Isopods*. Synopses of the British Fauna (New Series) No. 10. Published for the Linnean Society of London by Academic Press.

SMALDON, G. (1979). *British Coastal Shrimps and Prawns*. Synopses of the British Fauna (New Series) No. 15. Published for the Linnean Society of London and the Estuarine and Brackish Water Sciences Association by Cambridge University Press.

SOUTHWARD, A. J. and CRISP. D. J. (1963). *Catalogue of main marine fouling organisms, volume 1: Barnacles*. OECD Paris.

Molluscs

FRETTER, C. and GRAHAM, A. (1976–85). The Prosobranch Molluscs of Britain and Denmark. Nine parts published as supplements to *The Journal of Molluscan Studies*. [Well illustrated authoritative summaries of the biology of all operculate marine snails on the British list. Incorporating keys for identification.]

TEBBLE, Norman (1966). *British Bivalve Seashells*. British Museum (Natural History).

THOMPSON, T. E. and BROWN, Gregory H. (1976). *British Opisthobranch Molluscs*. Synopses of the British Fauna (New Series) No. 8. Published for the Linnean Society of London by Academic Press.

Bryozoans

RYLAND, J. S. and HAYWARD, P. J. (1977–85). *British Anascan Ctenostome* and *Cyclostome Bryozoans*. Four Synopses of the British Fauna (New Series). Published for the Linnean Society of London.

Freshwater Invertebrates

General

CROFT, P. S. (1986). A key to the major groups of freshwater intertebrates. *Field Studies*, **6**, 695–766.*

ENGELHARDT, Wolfgang (1964: 1973). *The young specialist looks at Pond Life*. Burke Books.

FITTER, R. and MANUEL, R. (1986). *Field guide to the Freshwater Life of Britain and North West Europe*. Collins.

MACAN, T. T. (1959). *A guide to Freshwater Invertebrate Animals*. Longman.

MELLANBY, Helen (1983). *Animal life in fresh water* 3rd Ed. Methuen.

READER'S DIGEST ASSOCIATION LTD. (1984). *Field Guide to the Water Life of Britain*. Reader's Digest.

Worms

BALL, Ian R. and REYNOLDSON, T. B. (1981). *British Planarians*. Synopses of the British Fauna (New Series) No. 19. Published for the Linnean Society of London and the Estuarine and Brackish Water Sciences Association by Cambridge University Press.

ELLIOTT, J. M. and MANN, K. H. (1979). *A key to the British Freshwater Leeches, with notes on their life cycles and ecology*. Freshwater Biological Association Publication No. 40.

REYNOLDSON, T. B. (1978). *A key to the British species of Freshwater Triclads* (Turbellaria, Paludicola). Freshwater Biological Association Scientific Publication No. 23.

Insects

AGUILAR, J., DOMMANGET, J.-L., and PRÉCHAC. (1986). *A field guide to the Dragonflies of Britain, Europe and North Africa*. Collins, London.

ASKEW, R. R. (1988). *The Dragonflies of Europe*. Harley Books, Colchester.

CRANSTON, P. S., RAMSDALE, C. D., SNOW, C. R. and WHITE, G. B. (1987). *Adults, larvae and pupae of British mosquitoes (Culicidae)*. Freshwater Biological Association Scientific Publication No. 48.

DAVIES, L. (1968). *A key to the British species of Simuliidae (Diptera) in the larval, pupal and adult stages*. Freshwater Biological Association Scientific Publication No. 24.

DISNEY, R. H. L. (1975). *A key to the larvae, pupae and adults of the British Dixidae (Diptera)*. Freshwater Biological Association Scientific Publication No. 31.

EDINGTON, J. M. & HILDREW, A. G. (1981). *A key to the Caseless Caddis Larvae of the British Isles, with notes on their ecology*. Freshwater Biological Association Scientific Publication No. 43.

ELLIOTT, J. M. (1977). *A key to the larvae and adults of British freshwater Megaloptera and Neuroptera*. Freshwater Biological Association Scientific Publication No. 35.

ELLIOTT, J. M. and HUMPESCH, U. H. (1983). *A key to the adults of British Ephemeroptera*. Freshwater Biological Association Scientific Publication No. 46.

FRIDAY, L. E. (1988). A key to adults of British Water Beetles. *Field Studies*, **7**, 1–151.*

GIBBONS, R. B. (1986). *Dragonflies and Damselflies of Britain and Northern Europe*. Country Life Books, Hamlyn, London.

MACAN, T. T. (1965). *A revised key to the British Water Bugs (Hemiptera–Heteroptera) with notes on their ecology*. Freshwater Biological Association Scientific Publication No. 16.

MACAN, T. T. (1961: 1979). *A key to the Nymphs of the British Species of Ephemeroptera, with notes on their ecology*. Freshwater Biological Association Scientific Publication No. 20.

MACAN, T. T. (1973). *A key to the adults of British Trichoptera*. Freshwater Biological Association Scientific Publication No. 28.

HAMMOND, C. O. (1985). *The Dragonflies of Great Britain and Ireland*. Harley Books, Colchester.

HICKEN, N. E. (1967). *Caddis Larvae*. Hutchinson, London.

HYNES, H. B. N. (1977). *A key to the adults and nymphs of the British Stoneflies (Plecoptera) with notes on their ecology and distribution*. Freshwater Biological Association Scientific Publication No. 17.

McGEERY, A. (1986). *A complete guide to British Dragonflies*. Jonathan Cape, London.

Arachnids

HOPKINS, C. L. (1961). A key to the Water Mites of the Flatford Area. *Field Studies*, **1**(3) 45–64.

Crustaceans

GLEDHILL, T., SUTCLIFFE, D. W. and WILLIAMS, W. D. (1976). *A key to the British Freshwater Crustacea Malacostraca*. Freshwater Biological Association Scientific Publication No. 32.

Molluscs

ELLIS, A. E. (1978). *British Freshwater Bivalve Mollusca*. Synopsis of the British Fauna No. 11 published for the Linnean Society of London by Academic Press.

FRETTER, V. and GRAHAM, A. (1978). The Prosobranch Molluscs of Britain and Denmark. Part 3. Neritacea, Viviparacea, Valvatacea, terrestrial and freshwater Littorinacea and Rissoacea. Published as a supplement to *The Journal of Molluscan Studies*.

MACAN, T. T. and COOPER, R. D. (1949: 1960). *A key to the British Fresh and Brackish Water Gastropods*. Freshwater Biological Association Scientific Publication No. 13.

Freshwater Fish

MAITLAND, P. S. (1972). *A key to the freshwater fishes of the British Isles*. F.B.A. Scientific Publication No. 27.

MUUS, B. J. and DAHLSTROM, P. (1971). *Collins guide to the Freshwater Fishes of Britain & Europe*. Collins.

Land Invertebrates

General

CLOUDSLEY-THOMPSON, J. L. and SANKEY, J. (1961). *Land Invertebrates*. Methuen.
[A guide to common land invertebrates other than insects.]

TILLING, S. M. (1987). A key to the major groups of terrestrial invertebrates. *Field Studies*, **6**, 695–766.*

Worms

SIMS, R. W. and GERARD, B. M. (1985). *Earthworms*. Synopsis of the British Fauna No 31. Published for the Linnean Society of London by E. J. Brill.

Insects

Royal Entomological Society of London. *Handbooks for the Identification of British Insects*.
[A series containing useful, but sometimes specialised, keys to insect families and species. Details from the Society at 41, Queens Gate, London SW7 5HU.]

BROWN, V. K. (1983). *Grasshoppers*. Naturalists' Handbooks No. 2. Cambridge University Press.

CHINERY, M. (1986). *A field guide to the Insects of Britain and Western Europe*. Collins.

DAVIS, B. N. K. (1983). *Insects on Nettles*. Naturalists' Handbooks No. 1. Cambridge University Press.

FORSYTHE, T. (1987). *Common Ground Beetles*. Naturalists' Handbooks, Richmond Publishing Company, Surrey.

GILBERT, F. S. (1986). *Hoverflies*. Naturalists' Handbooks, Cambridge University Press.

HARDE, K. W. and HAMMOND, P. W. (1984). *A field guide in colour to Beetles*. Octopus Books, London.

JOY, N. H. (1932). *A Practical Handbook of British Beetles* (2 vols) Reprinted 1976 by E. W. Classey Ltd, Faringdon, Oxon.

LEWIS, T. and TAYLOR, L. R. (1967). *Introduction to Experimental Ecology*. Academic Press.
[Contains useful keys to insect orders and families.]

PRŶS-JONES, O. E. and CORBET, S. A. (1987). *Bumblebees*. Naturalists' Handbooks, Cambridge University Press.

RAGGE, D. R. (1965). *Grasshoppers, Crickets and Cockroaches of the British Isles*. Warne.

READER'S DIGEST ASSOCIATION LTD. (1984). *Field Guide to the Butterflies and other Insects of Britain*. Reader's Digest.

REDFERN, Margaret (1983). *Insects and Thistles*. Naturalists' Handbooks No. 4. Cambridge University Press.

RICHARDS, O. W. (1977). *Hymenoptera: Introduction and key to the families*. Handbooks for the Identification of British Insects. Vol. 6, part 1, 2nd Edition. Royal Entomological Society of London.

SKIDMORE, Peter (1989). Insects of the Cowdung Community. Occasional publication of the Field Studies Council.*

SKINNER (1974). *Moths of the British Isles*. Viking Books, London.

SOUTHWOOD, T. R. E. and LESTON, D. (1959). *Land and Water Bugs of the British Isles*. Warne. (Wayside & Woodland Series).

STUBBS, A. E. and FALK, S. J. (1983). *British Hoverflies—an Illustrated Identification Guide*. British Entomological and Natural History Society.

THOMAS, J. A. (1986). *The RSNC guide to Butterflies of the British Isles.* Guild Publishing, London.

UNWIN, D. M. (1981). A key to the families of British Diptera. *Field Studies,* **5,** 513–533.*

UNWIN, D. M. (1984: 1988). A key to the families of British Coleoptera (and Strepsiptera). *Field Studies,* **6,** 149–197.*

WILLMER, Pat (1985). Bees, Ants and Wasps. A key to the genera of the British Aculeates. *Occasional Publication of the Field Studies Council No. 7.**

YEO, P. F. and CORBET, S. A. (1983). *Solitary Wasps.* Naturalists' Handbooks No. 3. Cambridge University Press.

Other Arthropods

BLOWER, J. G. (1985). *Millipedes.* Synopses of the British Fauna (New Series) No. 35. Linnean Society of London.

EASON, E. H. (1964). *Centipedes of the British Isles.* Warne.

HARDING, P. T. and SUTTON, S. L. (1985). *Woodlice in Britain and Ireland: distribution and habitats.* Institute of Terrestrial Ecology, Huntingdon PE17 2LS.

JONES, Dick (1983). *The Country Life Guide to Spiders of Britain and northern Europe.* Country Life Books.

LOCKET, G. H. and MILLIDGE, A. F. (1951–53). *British Spiders, Vols 1 & 2.* Ray Society, London.

LOCKET, G. H., MILLIDGE, A. F. and MERRETT, P. (1974). *British Spiders, Vol. 3.* Ray Society, London.

ROBERTS, M. J. (1984–). *The Spiders of Great Britain and Ireland.* 3 vols. Harley Books, Colchester.

SANKEY, J. H. P. and SAVORY, T. H. (1974). *British Harvestmen.* Synopses of the British Fauna (New Series) No. 4. Linnean Society of London.

SUTTON, S. L. (1972). *Woodlice,* Pergamon Press.

Molluscs

CAMERON, R. A. D., EVERSHAM, B. and JACKSON, N. (1983). A Field Key to the Slugs of the British Isles. *Field Studies,* **5,** 807–824.*

CAMERON, R. A. D. and REDFERN, M. (1976). *British land snails.* Synopses of the British Fauna (New Series) No. 6. Linnean Society of London.

KERNEY, M. P. and CAMERON, R. A. D. (1979). *A field guide to the Land Snails of Britain and north-west Europe.* Collins.

*Field Studies Council publications are available from:—FSC Publications, Preston Montford, Montford Bridge, Shrewsbury SY4 1HW, and at most of the FSC Field Centres.

Appendix II   Suppliers of field equipment and chemicals

General (mail-order only):

Bio-Science Supplies,
4 Long Mill North,
Wednesfield,
Woverhampton,
West Midlands WV11 1JD.

Watkins & Doncaster Ltd,
Four Throws,
Hawkhurst,
Kent.

Philip Harris Ltd,
Lynn Lane,
Shenstone,
Staffs WS14 0EE.

Arnold R. Horwell Ltd,
73 Maygrove Road,
West Hempstead,
London NW6 2BP.

Field equipment (nets, quadrats, range poles etc):

Educational Field Equipment,
1 Puddle,
Lanlivery,
Bodmin,
Cornwall PL30 5BY.
Tel. (0208) 872809.

Marris House Nets,
54 Richmond Park Avenue,
Bournemouth,
BH8 9DR.

Meters

W. P. A. Ltd,
The Old Station,
Linton,
Cambridge CB1 6NW.

Microscopes and Binoculars

Pyser Ltd,
Fircroft Way,
Edenbridge,
Kent TN8 6HA.

Technical and Optical Equipment Ltd,
Zenith House,
The Hyde,
Edgware Road,
London NW9 6EE.

Vickers Instruments,
Haxby Road,
York YO3 7SD.

Soil testing kits etc. (complete kits for pH measurement or mineral s estimates—NPK only; also replacement parts of kits and colour charts):

BDH Chemicals Ltd,
Broome Road,
Poole,
Dorset BH12 4NN.
Tel. (0202) 745520.

Pond nets

S. M. Davies,
45 Quest Hill Road,
Malvern,
Worcs WR14 IRL.
Tel. (06845) 65520.

Biological Water Sampling Equipment

G. B. Nets
Linden Bridge,
Hebden Bridge,
W. Yorks HX7 7DP
Tel (0422) 845365

Appendix III Statistical Tables

Table III(1) Random Numbers Table*

row no.						random numbers								
1	98	06	77	46	16	63	99	80	81	82	15	48	96	12	56
2	41	25	66	21	51	66	11	34	33	18	36	41	33	18	70
3	68	58	71	24	92	06	94	84	48	92	96	32	29	00	60
4	**78**	32	89	76	61	03	01	20	94	36	39	87	52	27	23
5	50	76	11	36	13	84	32	93	72	29	04	41	25	43	89
6	71	58	45	43	72	69	18	67	32	57	29	57	02	58	68
7	82	14	64	47	40	74	53	03	75	40	28	63	53	36	90
8	41	01	53	67	41	78	84	29	26	34	42	19	82	13	79
9	30	63	22	27	28	69	36	23	99	52	29	03	87	28	54
10	73	09	03	54	20	02	55	49	48	46	75	42	62	63	42
11	66	41	48	46	17	24	82	51	86	86	53	66	95	57	95
12	70	10	21	02	71	89	14	80	64	32	58	17	35	65	55
13	59	55	94	44	77	90	01	99	79	48	28	61	93	87	17
14	75	81	42	45	69	28	23	90	46	24	32	97	64	41	70
15	72	22	05	84	39	89	57	73	84	86	57	76	79	08	65
16	47	14	97	61	57	30	93	88	12	88	58	15	75	17	45
17	98	75	58	14	05	05	16	72	57	34	20	46	91	04	44
18	64	71	77	50	51	00	61	02	60	51	13	61	34	33	73
19	43	12	15	66	40	56	39	77	75	32	80	30	22	90	95
20	59	70	46	36	67	19	12	59	39	42	35	24	69	86	14
21	25	84	20	27	35	05	54	21	39	04	77	69	78	76	99
22	40	52	36	07	18	99	79	27	36	30	97	14	72	64	82
23	48	36	90	79	26	63	50	41	87	76	31	13	81	55	34
24	61	91	66	85	68	10	40	47	44	71	56	81	00	34	07
25	45	40	26	25	37	27	02	15	26	27	51	87	18	91	30
26	32	57	79	72	02	27	96	10	62	63	07	30	01	40	97
27	69	23	49	01	02	17	28	23	72	71	46	39	24	46	39
28	63	80	25	47	36	69	73	39	21	23	93	10	09	50	45
29	31	30	49	19	65	12	33	87	76	64	22	62	66	61	88
30	68	42	66	14	60	63	24	06	92	94	21	52	71	37	19
31	52	77	76	33	55	75	78	03	11	18	04	23	12	72	46
32	19	05	93	62	41	96	47	15	34	80	17	23	06	44	75
33	15	23	16	85	63	28	62	03	72	11	74	17	35	37	09
34	32	84	18	60	89	57	09	25	31	82	79	92	10	08	71
35	59	10	86	85	92	14	14	17	38	59	35	24	12	53	88
36	18	56	17	74	42	45	19	35	75	18	37	47	42	78	08
37	28	87	01	51	67	42	00	77	30	16	31	06	67	42	75
38	83	25	37	02	91	92	05	16	09	07	35	84	59	15	44
39	12	09	73	08	61	72	82	23	91	85	76	99	29	55	48
40	64	74	95	68	36	68	69	99	56	33	78	08	84	31	87
41	77	46	18	83	52	40	05	76	20	95	40	64	73	67	44
42	06	69	75	42	75	68	99	14	90	83	26	03	15	00	71
43	75	53	11	01	11	11	78	56	62	03	87	34	18	12	42
44	09	30	87	33	32	37	96	79	07	33	75	21	74	06	47
45	02	30	44	66	34	64	38	75	01	40	22	87	76	19	01
46	14	45	74	30	52	97	77	13	20	66	87	54	89	05	30
47	82	45	49	85	02	33	58	84	03	74	63	52	15	47	04
48	44	33	94	98	75	51	62	00	17	59	00	42	09	39	66
49	96	00	26	82	60	22	02	60	69	99	09	67	01	12	01
50	20	67	56	12	77	16	78	04	36	38	95	35	71	26	49

*A random series of the numbers 1 to 9 has been generated, in 50 rows of 30 digits. In the Table, the digits have been arranged in pairs, so that the first row contains the numbers 98, 06, 77, . . . , because this is the form in which they are needed in the Project Guide. Equally, however, they could be set out as 1-digit numbers (9, 8, 0 . . .), as 3-digit numbers (980, 677, 461 . . .), or in any form that your own project required.

Table III(2)   The Mann-Whitney U test

Critical values of U at the 5% level. Reject your null hypothesis at the 5% level if your value of U is less than or equal to the tabulated value.

n_1/n_2	1	2	3	4	5	6	7	8	9	10	11	12	13	14	15	16	17	18	19	20
1	—	—	—	—	—	—	—	—	—	—	—	—	—	—	—	—	—	—	—	—
2	—	—	—	—	—	—	—	0	0	0	0	1	1	1	1	1	2	2	2	2
3	—	—	—	—	0	1	1	2	2	3	3	4	4	5	5	6	6	7	7	8
4	—	—	—	0	1	2	3	4	4	5	6	7	8	9	10	11	11	12	13	13
5	—	—	0	1	2	3	5	6	7	8	9	11	12	13	14	15	17	18	19	20
6	—	—	1	2	3	5	6	8	10	11	13	14	16	17	19	21	22	24	25	27
7	—	—	1	3	5	6	8	10	12	14	16	18	20	22	24	26	28	30	32	34
8	—	0	2	4	6	8	10	13	15	17	19	22	24	26	29	31	34	36	38	41
9	—	0	2	4	7	10	12	15	17	20	23	26	28	31	34	37	39	42	45	48
10	—	0	3	5	8	11	14	17	20	23	26	29	33	36	39	42	45	48	52	55
11	—	0	3	6	9	13	16	19	23	26	30	33	37	40	44	47	51	55	58	62
12	—	1	4	7	11	14	18	22	26	29	33	37	41	45	49	53	57	61	65	69
13	—	1	4	8	12	16	20	24	28	33	37	41	45	50	54	59	63	67	72	76
14	—	1	5	9	13	17	22	26	31	36	40	45	50	55	59	64	67	74	78	83
15	—	1	5	10	14	19	24	29	34	39	44	49	54	59	64	70	75	80	85	90
16	—	1	6	11	15	21	26	31	37	42	47	53	59	64	70	75	81	86	92	98
17	—	2	6	11	17	22	28	34	39	45	51	57	63	67	75	81	87	93	99	105
18	—	2	7	12	18	24	30	36	42	48	55	61	67	74	80	86	93	99	106	112
19	—	2	7	13	19	25	32	38	45	52	58	65	72	78	85	92	99	106	113	119
20	—	2	8	13	20	27	34	41	48	55	62	69	76	83	90	98	105	112	119	127

Dashes indicate no decision possible at the stated level of significance.

Table III(3) The Wilcoxon matched pairs test

Critical values of W at various significance levels. Reject the null hypothesis if your value of W is less than the tabulated value at the chosen significance level, for the number of non-zero differences N_D.

N_D	significance level			
	10%	5%	2%	1%
5	0	—	—	—
6	2	0	—	—
7	3	2	0	—
8	5	3	1	0
9	8	5	3	1
10	10	8	5	3
11	13	10	7	5
12	17	13	9	7
13	21	17	12	9
14	25	21	15	12
15	30	25	19	15
16	35	29	23	19
17	41	34	27	23
18	47	40	32	27
19	53	46	37	32
20	60	52	43	37
21	67	58	49	42
22	75	65	55	48
23	83	73	62	54
24	91	81	69	61
25	100	89	76	68
26	110	98	84	75
27	119	107	92	83
28	130	116	101	91
29	140	126	110	100
30	151	137	120	109

Table III(4) The t test for matched and unmatched samples

Critical values of t at various significance levels. Reject the null hypothesis if your value of t is larger than the tabulated value at the chosen significance level, for the calculated number of degrees of freedom.

degrees of freedom	significance level					
	20%	10%	5%	2%	1%	0.1%
1	3·078	6·314	12·706	31·821	63·657	636·619
2	1·886	2·920	4·303	6·965	9·925	31·598
3	1·638	2·353	3·182	4·541	5·841	12·941
4	1·533	2·132	2·776	3·747	4·604	8·610
5	1·476	2·015	2·571	3·365	4·032	6·859
6	1·440	1·943	2·447	3·143	3·707	5·959
7	1·415	1·895	2·365	2·998	3·499	5·405
8	1·397	1·860	2·306	2·896	3·355	5·041
9	1·383	1·833	2·262	2·821	3·250	4·781
10	1·372	1·812	2·228	2·764	3·169	4·587
11	1·363	1·796	2·201	2·718	3·106	4·437
12	1·356	1·782	2·179	2·681	3·055	4·318
13	1·350	1·771	2·160	2·650	3·012	4·221
14	1·345	1·761	2·145	2·624	2·977	4·140
15	1·341	1·753	2·131	2·602	2·947	4·073
16	1·337	1·746	2·120	2·583	2·921	4·015
17	1·333	1·740	2·110	2·567	2·898	3·965
18	1·330	1·734	2·101	2·552	2·878	3·922
19	1·328	1·729	2·093	2·539	2·861	3·883
20	1·325	1·725	2·086	2·528	2·845	3·850
21	1·323	1·721	2·080	2·518	2·831	3·819
22	1·321	1·717	2·074	2·508	2·819	3·792
23	1·319	1·714	2·069	2·500	2·807	3·767
24	1·318	1·711	2·064	2·492	2·797	3·745
25	1·316	1·708	2·060	2·485	2·787	3·725
26	1·315	1·706	2·056	2·479	2·779	3·707
27	1·314	1·703	2·052	2·473	2·771	3·690
28	1·313	1·701	2·048	2·467	2·763	3·674
29	1·311	1·699	2·043	2·462	2·756	3·659
30	1·310	1·697	2·042	2·457	2·750	3·646
40	1·303	1·684	2·021	2·423	2·704	3·551
60	1·296	1·671	2·000	2·390	2·660	3·460
120	1·289	1·658	1·980	2·158	2·617	3·373
∞	1·282	1·645	1·960	2·326	2·576	3·291

Table III(5). The χ^2 test for association

Critical values of χ^2 at various significance levels. Reject the null hypothesis if your value of χ^2 is bigger than the tabulated value at the chosen significance level, for the calculated number of degrees of freedom.

degrees of freedom	significance level:												
	99%	98%	95%	90%	80%	70%	50%	30%	20%	10%	5%	2%	1%
1	0·000157	0·000628	0·00393	0·0158	0·0642	0·148	0·455	1·074	1·642	2·706	3·841	5·412	6·635
2	0·0201	0·0404	0·103	0·211	0·446	0·713	1·386	2·408	3·219	4·605	5·991	7·824	9·210
3	0·115	0·185	0·352	0·584	1·005	1·424	2·366	3·665	4·642	6·251	7·815	9·837	11·341
4	0·297	0·429	0·711	1·064	1·649	2·195	3·357	4·878	5·989	7·779	9·488	11·668	13·277
5	0·554	0·752	1·145	1·610	2·343	3·000	4·351	6·064	7·289	9·236	1·070	13·388	15·086
6	0·872	1·134	1·635	2·204	3·070	3·828	5·348	7·231	8·558	10·645	12·592	15·033	16·812
7	1·239	1·564	2·167	2·833	3·822	4·671	6·346	8·383	9·803	12·017	14·067	16·622	18·475
8	1·646	2·032	2·733	3·490	4·594	5·527	7·344	9·524	11·030	13·362	15·507	18·168	20·090
9	2·088	2·532	3·325	4·168	5·380	6·393	8·343	10·656	12·242	14·684	16·919	19·679	21·666
10	2·558	3·059	3·940	4·865	6·179	7·267	9·342	11·781	13·442	15·987	18·307	21·161	23·209
11	3·053	3·609	4·575	5·578	6·989	8·148	10·341	12·899	14·631	17·275	19·675	22·618	24·725
12	3·571	4·178	5·226	6·304	7·807	9·034	11·340	14·011	15·812	18·549	21·026	24·054	26·217
13	4·107	4·765	5·892	7·042	8·634	9·926	12·340	15·119	16·985	19·812	22·362	25·472	27·688
14	4·660	5·368	6·571	7·790	9·467	10·821	13·339	16·222	18·151	21·064	23·685	26·873	29·141
15	5·229	5·985	7·261	8·547	10·307	11·721	14·339	17·322	19·311	22·307	24·996	28·259	30·578
16	5·812	6·614	7·962	9·312	11·152	12·624	15·338	18·418	20·465	23·542	26·296	29·633	32·000
17	6·408	7·255	8·672	10·085	12·002	13·531	16·338	19·511	21·615	24·769	27·587	30·995	33·409
18	7·015	7·906	9·390	10·865	12·857	14·440	17·338	20·601	22·760	25·989	28·869	32·346	34·805
19	7·633	8·567	10·117	11·651	13·716	15·352	18·338	21·689	23·900	27·204	30·144	33·687	36·191
20	8·260	9·237	10·851	12·443	14·578	16·266	19·337	22·775	25·038	28·412	31·410	35·020	37·566
21	8·897	9·915	11·594	13·240	15·445	17·182	20·337	23·858	26·171	29·615	32·671	36·343	38·932
22	9·542	10·600	12·338	14·041	16·314	18·101	21·337	24·939	27·301	30·813	33·924	37·659	40·289
23	10·196	11·293	13·091	14·848	17·187	19·021	22·337	26·018	28·429	32·007	35·172	38·968	41·638
24	10·856	11·992	13·848	15·659	18·062	19·943	23·337	27·096	29·553	33·196	36·415	40·270	42·980
25	11·524	12·697	14·611	16·473	18·940	20·867	24·337	28·172	30·675	34·382	37·652	41·566	44·314
26	12·198	13·409	15·379	17·292	19·820	21·792	25·336	29·246	31·795	35·563	38·885	42·856	45·642
27	12·879	14·125	16·151	18·114	20·703	22·719	26·336	30·319	32·912	36·741	40·113	44·140	46·963
28	13·565	14·847	16·928	18·939	21·588	23·647	27·336	31·391	34·027	37·916	41·337	45·419	48·278
29	14·256	15·574	17·708	19·768	22·475	24·577	28·336	32·461	35·139	39·087	42·557	46·693	49·588
30	14·953	16·306	18·493	20·599	23·364	25·508	29·336	33·530	36·250	40·256	43·773	47·962	50·892

Table III(6)   The Spearman rank correlation coefficient, r_S

Critical values of r_S at various significance levels. Reject the null hypothesis if your value of r_S is greater than or equal to than the tabulated value at the chosen significance level, for your number of pairs, n.

no. of pairs, n	significance level:			
	10%	5%	2%	1%
5	0·900	1·000	1·000	—
6	0·829	0·886	0·943	1·000
7	0·714	0·786	0·893	0·929
8	0·643	0·738	0·833	0·881
9	0·600	0·683	0·783	0·833
10	0·564	0·648	0·746	0·794
12	0·506	0·591	0·712	0·777
14	0·456	0·544	0·645	0·715
16	0·425	0·506	0·601	0·665
18	0·399	0·475	0·564	0·625
20	0·377	0·450	0·534	0·591
22	0·359	0·428	0·508	0·562
24	0·343	0·409	0·485	0·537
26	0·329	0·392	0·465	0·515
28	0·317	0·377	0·448	0·496
30	0·306	0·364	0·432	0·478

Appendix IV   List of symbols used in Project Guide

c — point at which the straight line, in linear regression, cuts the vertical axis:

$$c = \bar{y} - m\bar{x}$$

$\overline{D}$ — mean of differences between matched pairs of measurements

ΣD^2 — sum of squared differences in ranks of matched pairs of measurements

E — frequencies expected under a null hypothesis of no association in the χ^2 test

H_0 — null hypothesis

H_1 — alternative hypothesis

m — slope of the straight line in linear regression of y on x:

$$m = \frac{\Sigma(x - \bar{x})(y - \bar{y})}{\Sigma(x - \bar{x})^2}$$

μ — (Greek mu) population mean

μ_A — mean of population A

N — total number in population

N_D — number of rank differences that are not zero

n — sample size

n_A — size of sample A

O — observed frequencies in χ^2 test

r_S — Spearman rank correlation coefficient:

$$r_S = 1 - \frac{6\Sigma D^2}{n(n^2 - 1)}$$

s — sample standard deviation:

$$s = \sqrt{\frac{\Sigma(x - \bar{x})^2}{n-1}} \quad \text{or} \quad \sqrt{\frac{\Sigma x^2 - (\Sigma x)^2/n}{n-1}}$$

s^2 sample variance:

$$s^2 = \frac{\Sigma(x - \bar{x})^2}{n} \quad \text{or} \quad \frac{\Sigma x^2}{n} - x^2$$

s_A^2 variance of sample A

s_C^2 estimate of the common population variance:

$$S_C^2 = \frac{(n_A - 1)s_A^2 + (n_B - 1)s_B^2}{(n_A - 1) + (n_B - 1)}$$

s_D^2 sample variance of the difference in paired measurements from matched samples.

SE_D standard error of the difference in sample means:

$$SE_D = \sqrt{\frac{s_A^2}{n_A} + \frac{s_B^2}{n_B}}$$

(for unmatched samples where n_A and n_B are both > 25)

$$SE_D = \sqrt{\frac{S_C^2}{n_A} + \frac{S_C^2}{n_B}}$$

(for unmatched samples where n_A and n_B are $\leqslant 25$)

$$SE_D = \sqrt{\frac{s_D^2}{n}}$$

(for matched samples)

s.e.m.   standard error of the mean

Σ (Greek sigma) sum of all the numbers

t the test statistic for the t test

$$t = \frac{\bar{x}_A - \bar{x}_B}{SE_D} \text{ (for unmatched samples)}$$

$$t = \frac{\bar{D}}{SE_D} \text{ (for matched samples)}$$

U test statistic for Mann–Whitney U test

W test statistic for Wilcoxon matched pairs test

x an individual measurement

Σx sum of the numbers symbolized by the letter x

Σx^2 sum of the squares of the numbers symbolized by the letter x

$\bar{x}_A$ mean of sample A

$$\bar{x}_A = \frac{\Sigma x}{n}$$

χ^2 (Greek chi) test statistic for the χ^2 test

$$\chi^2 = \Sigma \frac{(O - E)^2}{E}$$

z test statistic in the z test:

$$z = \frac{\bar{x}_A - \bar{x}_B}{SE_D} - \mu \text{ (for unmatched samples)}$$

$$z = \frac{\bar{D}}{SE_D} \text{ (for matched samples)}$$

Index

Acknowledgements
Grateful acknowledgement is made to the following for
permission to reproduce Tables in this Guide.

Table III (2) R. C. Campbell (1974) *Statistics for Biologists,*
Cambridge University Press.

Tables III (3), III (4), III (5), III (6). A. Haber and
R. P. Runyon (1973) *General Statistics.* Addison-Wesley
Publishing.